Y0-CBC-838

BASIC SKILLS WITH MATH

BASIC SKILLS WITH MATH

Ratios & Percents

Jerry Howett

CAMBRIDGE ADULT EDUCATION

Upper Saddle River, New Jersey

www.globefearon.com/welcome/cambridge.html

EDITORIAL DEVELOPER: Cathy Fillmore Hoyt

EDITORS: Stephanie Cahill, Doug Falk, Dena Pollak, Phyllis Dunsay

PRODUCTION EDITOR: Alan Dalgleish, Suzanne Keezer

BOOK DESIGN: Parallelogram, New York

ELECTRONIC PAGE PRODUCTION: Burmar Technical Corporation, Albertson, New York

COVER ART: Salem Krieger

COVER DESIGN: Patricia Battipede

Copyright © 1999 by Globe Fearon, Inc. 1 Lake Street, Upper Saddle River, New Jersey 07458. All rights reserved. No part of this book may be reproduced or transmitted in any form or by any means, electronic, photographic, mechanical, or otherwise, including photocopying, recording, or by any information storage and retrieval system, without permission in writing from the publisher.

Printed in the United States of America

1 2 3 4 5 6 7 8 9 10   02 01 00 99 98

ISBN 0-835-95731-4

CAMBRIDGE ADULT EDUCATION
Upper Saddle River, New Jersey
www.globefearon.com/welcome/cambridge.html

▼ Contents

Ratios & Percents Preview...1

Unit 1. Ratio

What Is a Ratio? 6
Writing Ratios from Words 8
Simplifying Ratios 11
Ratio of Measurements 13
Ratio Review...18

Unit 2. Proportion

What Is a Proportion? 20
Solving Proportions..23
Proportion Shortcuts 27
Map Scales 29
Finding Unit Rates 31
Multi-Step Proportions..33
Proportion Review 35

Unit 3. Understanding Percent

What Is a Percent?..37
Changing Decimals to Percents 39
Changing Percents to Decimals 40
Changing Fractions to Percents 42
Changing Percents to Fractions 43
Common Fractions, Decimals, and Percents............46
Identifying the Percent, the Whole and the Part......48
Understanding Percent Review 51

Unit 4. Finding the Part

Finding the Part..53
Using Proportion to Find the Part 56
Rounding Money 58
Less than 1% 60
More than 100% 61
Quick Answers..62
Using Circle Graphs 63
Interest..66
Multi-Step Problems..69
Finding the Part Review 72

Unit 5. Finding the Percent and the Whole

Finding What Percent One Number Is of Another..........................75

Using Proportion to Find the Percent 79

Percent of Increase 81

Percent of Decrease 83

Finding a Number When a Percent of It Is Given 85

Using Proportion to Find the Whole..88

Mixed Percent Problems..90

Finding the Percent and the Whole Review 93

Final Review..95

Answers...101

RATIOS & PERCENTS
PREVIEW

The problems on pages 1 through 5 will help you find out which parts of this book you need to work on. Do all the problems you can. At the end of the problems, look at the chart on page 5 to see which page you should go to next.

Use the following information to answer questions 1 and 2.

There are 5 paid employees and 6 volunteers working in the cafeteria of the Westbrook School.

1. What is the ratio of the number of paid employees to the number of volunteers?

2. What is the ratio of the number of paid employees to the total number of workers?

For problems 3 to 5, simplify each ratio.

3. 16:24   4. 35 to 25   5. 3:30

6. Simplify the ratio of 3 months to 1 year.

7. Simplify the ratio of 14 inches to 2 feet.

For problems 8 to 10, solve each proportion for x.

8. $\dfrac{9}{10} = \dfrac{x}{4}$ 9. $\dfrac{12}{x} = \dfrac{8}{15}$ 10. $x:3 = 2:9$

11. Maxine drove 92 miles in 2 hours. If she drives at the same rate, how far can she go in 5 hours?

12. The scale on a map is 1 inch = 24 miles. Two towns are 3.5 inches apart on the map. What is the distance in miles between the towns?

13. Conrad paid $9.79 for 2.2 pounds of pork. What was the price per pound?

14. The ratio of men to women at Mike's Trucking Company is 5:2. There are 28 employees altogether. How many women work at Mike's?

Change each decimal to a percent.

15. .4 =

16. .04 =

17. .225 =

Change each percent to a decimal.

18. 9% =

19. $3\frac{1}{3}\% =$

20. 250% =

Change each fraction to a percent.

21. $\frac{13}{20} =$

22. $\frac{7}{16} =$

23. $\frac{9}{50} =$

Change each percent to a fraction.

24. 16% =

25. 4.5% =

26. $44\frac{4}{9}\% =$

27. Find 30% of 70.

28. Find 25% of 124.

29. Find $37\frac{1}{2}\%$ of 64.

30. Find $83\frac{1}{3}\%$ of 300.

31. Find 150% of 18.

32. Find 0.75% of 480.

33. The Johnsons make $28,000 a year. They spend 30% of their income for food. How much do they spend on food in a year?

34. In 1980 there were 230,000 people living in Central County. In 1995 the number of people in the county was 110% of the 1980 number. How many people lived in Central County in 1995?

35. Find 6% of $7.49. Round off to the nearest cent.

The circle graph shows the expenses of a youth services program. Use the graph to answer questions 36 and 37.

36. What percent of the program's expenses go to fund raising?

37. The annual expenses for the program are $500,000. What amount goes to management and general expenses?

Expenses

82.9%
Program Services

9.7%
Fund Raising

7.4%
Management
& General

38. Harry bought a pair of shorts for $19.50. The sales tax in his state is 8%. How much did Harry pay for the shorts, including the sales tax?

39. Valerie makes $420 a week. Her employer takes out 17% of her check for taxes and social security. How much does Valerie take home in a week?

40. Find the interest on $800 at 6% annual interest for one year.

41. Find the interest on $800 at 6.5% annual interest for one year and three months.

42. 14 is what % of 35?

43. 80 is what % of 120?

44. 36 is what % of 40?

45. 16 is what % of 50?

46. Last year Sam weighed 240 pounds. He went on a diet and lost 24 pounds. What percent of his weight did Sam lose?

47. Mary works 40 hours a week. She spends about 24 hours every week making deliveries. What percent of her work week does Mary spend making deliveries?

48. In 1980 there were 4 members in Mr. and Mrs. Miller's family. In 1995 there were 7 members. By what percent did the size of the family increase?

49. Frank bought new tires on sale for $85. Before the sale the tires cost $100. Find the percent of discount on the original price.

50. $33\frac{1}{3}$% of what number is 45?

51. 37.5% of what number is 36?

52. 75% of what number is 90?

53. 35% of what number is 49?

54. 75% of the members of a firemen's union voted to strike. 126 members voted to strike. How many members are there in the union?

55. Tom spends $270 a month on payments for his car loan. The payments are 15% of his income. How much does Tom make in a month?

PROGRESS CHECK

Check your answers on page 101. Then complete the chart below.

Problem numbers	Number of problems in this section	Number of problems you got right in this section	
1 to 7	7	_____	If you had fewer than 5 problems right, go to page 6.
8 to 14	7	_____	If you had fewer than 5 problems right, go to page 20.
15 to 26	12	_____	If you had fewer than 9 problems right, go to page 37.
27 to 41	15	_____	If you had fewer than 11 problems right, go to page 53.
42 to 55	14	_____	If you had fewer than 11 problems right, go to page 75.

Ratio

What Is a Ratio?

There are two common ways to compare numbers. One method uses subtraction. The other uses division.

Jed is 27 years old, and Adriana is 25. One way to compare their ages is to subtract: $27 - 25 = 2$. Jed is *two years older* than Adriana.

Adriana makes $16 an hour at her job, and Jed makes $8 an hour at his. One way to compare their wages is to divide: $16 \div 8 = 2$. Adriana makes *two times or twice as much* an hour as Jed. This means that for every $2 that Adriana makes, Jed makes $1.

A **ratio** is a comparison of numbers by division. A ratio can be written with the word *to*, with a colon (:), or as a fraction. The fraction method is most common. The first number in a ratio is the numerator (top number). The second number is the denominator (bottom number).

The ratio of Adriana's wage to Jed's wage is 2 to 1. The ratio can also be written as 2:1 or as $\frac{2}{1}$.

In each case, read the ratio as, "two to one."

PRACTICE I

Use the ratio 5:2 to answer questions 1 to 7.

1. Rewrite the ratio with the word *to*.

2. Rewrite the ratio as a fraction.

3. Which number is the numerator?

4. Which number is the denominator?

5. The ratio 5:2 is the ratio of the number of days Marlene works each week to the number of days she has free. For every 5 days she works, how many does she have free?

6. What is the ratio of the number of days Marlene has free to the number of days she works? Write the ratio as a fraction.

7. Rewrite the ratio in problem 6 with the word *to*.

The illustration represents the number of men and women in Paulo's English as a second language class. Use the illustration to answer questions 8 to 15.

8. How many women are in the class?

9. How many men are in the class?

10. What is the total number of students in the class?

For problems 11 to 14, write each ratio with a colon.

11. What is the ratio of men to women?

12. What is the ratio of women to men?

13. What is the ratio of the number of women to the total number of students?

14. What is the ratio of the number of men to the total number of students?

For problem 15, write a number in each blank to make the statement true.

15. For every _____ women in the class, there are_____ men.

To check your answers, turn to page 101.

Writing Ratios from Words

Joan makes $18 an hour at Ace Electric Supply. When she started working at Ace, she made $7 an hour. What is the ratio of Joan's wage now to the wage she made when she started working at Ace?

Example: Write a ratio of Joan's current wage of $18 an hour to her starting wage of $7 an hour.

STEP 1.   Write the first number mentioned, 18, as the numerator. $\dfrac{18}{}$

STEP 2.   Write the second number, 7, as the denominator. $\dfrac{18}{7}$

⟹   The ratio of Joan's current wage to her starting wage is $\dfrac{18}{7}$ or 18:7 or 18 to 7.

8   Ratios & Percents

PRACTICE 2

A. For problems 1 to 6, write each ratio as a fraction.

1. 83 miles in 2 hours

2. 1 teacher for 25 students

3. 3 for $1.99

4. 5 gallons for 2 walls

5. $25 for 3 CDs

6. 2 cups for 3 pounds

For problems 7 to 12, write each ratio with a colon (:).

7. 4 runs in 9 innings

8. $28 for 3 people

9. 800 people in 5 days

10. 100 calls in 7 hours

11. 1 ounce for 5 gallons

12. 2 guards for 135 children

Many ratios express an amount for a single unit. The phrase *miles per gallon* means miles for every 1 gallon. The phrase *customers an hour* means customers for every 1 hour.

Example: Sam gets 28 miles per gallon. Write his gas mileage as a ratio.

➠ Sam's gas mileage is $\frac{28}{1}$.

B. For problems 13 to 18, write each ratio as a fraction.

13. 55 miles an hour

14. 26 miles a gallon

15. 24 cans per case

16. $9 an hour

17. 4 feet per shelf

18. 3 pairs per package

For problems 19 to 24, write each ratio with the word *to*.

19. 50 envelopes per pack

20. $9,500 a student

21. 144 sheets a box

22. $25 an ounce

23. 2 tickets each

24. 10 acres per lot

Use the following situation to answer questions 25 to 29.

At Ace Electric Supply there are 13 full-time employees and 6 part-time employees.

25. Write with a colon (:) the ratio of the number of full-time employees at Ace to the number of part-time employees.

26. Write with the word *to* the ratio of the number of part-time employees to the number of full-time employees.

27. What is the total number of employees at Ace Electric Supply?

28. Write as a fraction the ratio of the number of full-time employees to the total number of employees.

29. Write as a fraction the ratio of the number of part-time employees to the total number of employees.

To check your answers, turn to page 102.

Simplifying Ratios

In Joanna's office there are 12 clerks and 8 administrative assistants. What is the ratio of clerks to assistants in the office?

Like a fraction, a ratio can be simplified or reduced. To simplify a ratio, find a number that divides evenly into both the numerator (first number) and the denominator (second number). Remember that simplifying changes the numbers in a ratio, but it does not change the value.

Example: Simplify the ratio 12 to 8.

STEP 1. Divide both 12 and 8 by a number that divides evenly into both of them. 4 divides evenly into both 12 and 8.

$$\frac{12 \div 4}{8 \div 4} = \frac{3}{2}$$

STEP 2. Check to see if another number, besides 1, divides evenly into 3 and 2. No other number divides evenly into both. The ratio 3:2 is simplified as far as it can be.

➡ The ratio of clerks to assistants in Joanna's office is 3:2.

PRACTICE 3

For problems 1 to 12, simplify each ratio.

1. 15:25

2. 36:45

3. 21:56

4. 32:40

5. 13 to 26

6. 18 to 2

7. 4 to 48

8. 27 to 30

9. $\dfrac{12}{60}$

10. $\dfrac{22}{20}$

11. $\dfrac{5}{1,000}$

12. $\dfrac{250}{25}$

For problems 13 to 18, simplify each ratio. Ignore the units, and write each ratio with a colon (:).

13. 52 miles to 2 gallons

14. 45 calls in 3 hours

15. 2 tickets for $30

16. 4 pounds for 10 people

17. 200 parts in 8 hours

18. 300 students in 10 classrooms

For the next problems, write each ratio as a fraction, and simplify each ratio.

Use the following information for questions 19 to 22.

So far, Mark has paid $1,600 on his car loan. He still has to pay $800.

19. What is the ratio of the amount Mark has paid to the amount he still has to pay?

20. What is the ratio of the amount Mark still has to pay to the amount he has already paid?

21. Write a ratio for the amount Mark has paid on his loan to the total amount of the loan. [**Hint:** To find the total amount of the loan, add the amount Mark has paid to the amount he has left to pay.]

22. Write a ratio for the amount Mark still has to pay on his loan to the total amount of the loan.

Use the following information to answer questions 23 and 24.

> To get the right color for her house, Kate mixed six gallons of green paint and two gallons of white paint.

23. What was the ratio of green paint to the total amount of paint?

24. What was the ratio of white paint to the total amount of paint?

To check your answers, turn to page 102.

Ratio of Measurements

Kelly works at an appliance repair shop. He estimates that he spends 12 minutes out of every hour talking to customers. What is the ratio of the time Kelly spends talking to customers to the total time he spends in the shop?

To compare units of measurement, express them in the same terms. To compare minutes and hours, change both to minutes.

Example: Simplify the ratio of 12 minutes to one hour.

STEP 1. Change 1 hour to minutes.   12 min:1 hr = 12:60
         One hour = 60 minutes.

STEP 2. Divide 12 and 60 by a number   12:60 = 1:5
         that divides evenly into both, 12.

⟱ The ratio of the time Kelly spends talking to customers to the total time he spends at work is 1:5.

Use the following table of time measurements to solve problems 1 to 13.

Time
1 minute (min) = 60 seconds (sec)
1 hour (hr) = 60 min
1 day (d) = 24 hr
1 week (wk) = 7 days
1 year (yr) = 365 days = 12 months

Write each ratio with a colon (:) and simplify.

1. 20 minutes to an hour

2. 8 months to 1 year

3. 8 hours to 1 day

4. 10 seconds to 1 minute

5. 6 days to 2 weeks

6. 30 months to 1 year

7. 30 hours to 1 day

8. 2 days to 4 weeks

9. 1 month to 3 years

10. 1 day to 100 hours

The table below shows the driving times for four city busses. It tells the scheduled time for each bus run and the actual performance (Minutes Late) one day. Use the table to answer questions 11 to 13.

Bus Line	Scheduled Run	Minutes Late
A	2 hr 30 min	30 min
B	4 hr	48 min
C	1 hr 20 min	0 min
D	1 hr 40 min	12 min

11. For Bus Line A what was the ratio of the number of minutes late to the scheduled run?

12. For Line B what was the ratio of the number of minutes late to the scheduled run?

13. Find the ratio of minutes late to scheduled run for Line D.

Use the following table of length measurements to solve problems 14 to 23.

Length
1 foot (ft) = 12 inches (in.)
1 yard (yd) = 3 ft = 36 in.
1 mile (mi) = 5,280 ft = 1,760 yd

Write each ratio as a fraction and simplify.

14. 8 inches to 1 foot

15. 1 foot to 1 yard

16. 1 mile to 2,640 feet

17. 2 feet to 16 inches

18. 3 yards to 15 feet

19. 9 inches to 4 feet

20. 30 inches to 1 yard

21. 1 mile to 528 feet

22. 5 feet to 100 inches

23. 8 feet to 2 yards

The drawings show the height and length of brick (including mortar) and the height and length of a garden wall. Use the dimensions to answer questions 24 and 25.

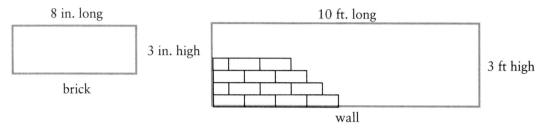

24. What is the ratio of the height of one brick to the height of the garden wall?

25. What is the ratio of the length of one brick to the length of the garden wall?

Use the following table of liquid measurements to solve problems 26 to 32.

> *Liquid Measure*
> 1 cup = 8 fluid ounces (fl oz)
> 1 pint (pt) = 2 cups = 16 fluid ounces
> 1 quart (qt) = 2 pints = 32 fluid ounces
> 1 gallon (gal) = 4 quarts

Write each ratio with the word *to* and simplify.

26. 1 quart to 1 gallon

27. 20 fluid ounces to 1 pint

28. 2 gallons to 3 quarts

29. 1 cup to 10 fluid ounces

30. 5 quarts to 1 pint

31. 1 quart to 3 cups

32. The instructions on a bottle of concentrated cleanser guaranteed to remove most oil stains require mixing 1 cup of cleanser with 5 gallons of warm water. What is the ratio of cleanser to water in the mixture?

Use the following table of weight measurements to solve problems 33 to 42.

Weight
1 pound (lb) = 16 ounces (oz)
1 ton = 2,000 pounds

Write each ratio as a fraction and simplify.

33. 12 ounces to 1 pound

34. 500 pounds to 1 ton

35. 20 ounces to 2 pounds

36. 5,000 pounds to 2 tons

37. 4 ounces to 3 pounds

38. 1 ton to 100 pounds

39. 30 ounces to 1 pound

40. 1,500 pounds to 3 tons

41. A tin of cookies weighs 4 ounces. A box of cookies weighs 2 pounds. What is the ratio of the weight of a tin of cookies to the weight of a box of cookies?

42. An older submarine displaces 1,600 tons of water when it goes under the water. A newer design displaces only 1,400 tons of water when submerged. What is the ratio of the newer submarine's weight to the heavier submarine's weight? [**Hint:** The amount of water displaced is equal to the submarine's weight.]

To check your answers, turn to page 102.

Ratio Review

The problems on pages 18 and 19 will help you find out if you need to review the ratio section of this book. When you finish, look at the chart to see which pages you should review.

Use the information below to answer questions 1 and 2.

> The ratio of the amount of money the Garcias spend on food to the amount they take home is 3:10.

1. Fill in the blanks: For every _____ dollars the Garcias

   spend on food, they bring home _____ dollars.

2. What is the ratio of the amount the Garcias take home to the amount they spend on food?

Use the information below to answer questions 3 and 4.

> For every 99 good bottles produced at Premier Plastics, one bottle is defective.

3. What is the ratio of good bottles to defective bottles?

4. What is the ratio of defective bottles to total bottles produced?

For problems 5 to 10, simplify each ratio.

5. 9:12

6. 84 miles in 2 hours

7. 35 to 14

8. 18 people in 4 cars

9. 10 inches to 1 foot

10. 40 minutes to 2 hours

PROGRESS CHECK

Check your answers on page 103. Then return to the review pages for the problems you missed. Correct your answers before going on to the next unit.

If you missed problems	Review pages
1 to 2	6 to 7
3 to 4	8 to 10
5 to 8	11 to 12
9 to 10	13 to 17

Proportion

What Is a Proportion?

A **proportion** is a statement that two ratios are equal. The statement $\frac{9}{12} = \frac{3}{4}$ is a proportion. A proportion is the same as two equal fractions. Each of the four numbers in a ratio (or a pair of equal fractions) is called a **term.**

The **cross products** in a proportion are equal. This means that the top term of the first ratio times the bottom term of the second equals the bottom term of the first ratio times the top term of the second. For the proportion $\frac{9}{12} = \frac{3}{4}$, one cross product is 9×4, and the other is 12×3. Both cross products equal 36.

$$\frac{9}{12} \diagdown\!\!\!\!\diagup \frac{3}{4}$$

$$9 \times 4 = 12 \times 3$$

$$36 = 36$$

PRACTICE 5

Answer each question.

Use the fractions $\frac{5}{2}$ and $\frac{20}{8}$ to answer questions 1 to 4.

1. What is the cross product of 5 and 8?

$$\frac{5}{2} \diagup\!\!\!\!\diagdown \frac{20}{8}$$

2. What is the cross product of 2 and 20?

3. Are the cross products equal?

4. Do the fractions make a proportion?

Use the fractions $\frac{6}{13}$ and $\frac{1}{2}$ to answer questions 5 to 8.

5. What is the cross product of 6 and 2? $\frac{6}{13} \diagdown \frac{1}{2}$

6. What is the cross product of 13 and 1?

7. Are the cross products equal?

8. Do the fractions make a proportion?

For the proportions in 9 to 11, write the terms in each cross product. Then write the answer to each cross product. The first proportion is written as an example.

9. $\frac{4}{5} = \frac{8}{10}$ $\frac{7}{4} = \frac{21}{12}$ $\frac{15}{10} = \frac{6}{4}$

   $4 \times 10 = 5 \times 8$
   $40 = 40$

10. $\frac{6}{18} = \frac{1}{3}$ $\frac{2}{7} = \frac{8}{28}$ $\frac{24}{6} = \frac{4}{1}$

11. $\frac{2}{5} = \frac{8}{20}$ $\frac{108}{9} = \frac{12}{1}$ $\frac{7}{9} = \frac{21}{27}$

For problems 12 and 13, first rewrite each proportion with fractions. Then write the terms in each cross product and the answer to each cross product. The first proportion is written as an example.

12. $5:25 = 10:50$ $16:6 = 8:3$ $4:1 = 36:9$

$$\frac{5}{25} = \frac{10}{50}$$

$5 \times 50 = 25 \times 10$

$250 = 250$

13. $30:70 = 3:7$ $1:8 = 6:48$ $12:9 = 16:12$

Use the information below to answer questions 14 to 16.

On a quiz with five questions, Jamal got four questions right. On a test with 20 questions, he got 16 right.

14. What is the ratio of the number of questions on the *quiz* to the number that Jamal got right?

15. What is the ratio of the number of questions on the *test* to the number that Jamal got right?

16. Do the two ratios make a proportion? Why or why not?

To check your answers, turn to page 104.

Solving Proportions

The ratio of salespeople to cashiers in Akim's store is 3:2. There are 12 salespeople in the store. How many cashiers work there?

Proportion is a useful way to solve many word problems. In most proportion problems, one of the four terms is missing. Use a letter to stand for the missing term.

When a term is missing in a proportion, only one cross product can be completed. The other cross product is incomplete. To find the missing term, divide the *completed* cross product by the number in the *incomplete* cross product.

Example: Find the number of cashiers in Akim's store.

STEP 1.   Set the proportion up carefully. Write labels to identify the terms. Notice that the number of salespeople, 12, goes on top. Use the letter c to represent the number of cashiers.

$$\frac{\text{salespeople}}{\text{cashiers}} \quad \frac{3}{2} = \frac{12}{c}$$

$$\frac{3}{2} \diagdown \frac{12}{c}$$

STEP 2.   Cross multiply. The cross product of 3 and c is $3 \times c$. The cross product of 2 and 12 is 24.

$$3 \times c = 2 \times 12$$
$$3 \times c = 24$$

STEP 3.   To find c, divide 24 by the number in the incomplete cross product, 3.

$$c = 24 \div 3$$
$$c = 8$$

⟾   There are 8 cashiers in Akim's store.

PRACTICE 6

A. Solve each problem.

In problems 1 to 3, solve each proportion for the letter a.

1. $\dfrac{5}{6} = \dfrac{15}{a}$ $\qquad\qquad$ $\dfrac{10}{8} = \dfrac{a}{16}$ $\qquad\qquad$ $\dfrac{4}{a} = \dfrac{12}{18}$

2. $\dfrac{a}{40} = \dfrac{6}{20}$ $\qquad\qquad$ $\dfrac{5}{3} = \dfrac{25}{a}$ $\qquad\qquad$ $\dfrac{18}{21} = \dfrac{a}{7}$

3. $\dfrac{2}{a} = \dfrac{8}{12}$ $\qquad\qquad$ $\dfrac{14}{7} = \dfrac{12}{a}$ $\qquad\qquad$ $\dfrac{a}{10} = \dfrac{27}{30}$

For problems 4 to 6, rewrite each proportion as two fractions. Then solve each proportion for the letter x.

4. $7:4 = 28:x$ $\qquad\qquad$ $2:9 = x:45$ $\qquad\qquad$ $6:x = 30:40$

5. $x:24 = 7:3$ $\qquad\qquad$ $22:16 = 11:x$ $\qquad\qquad$ $45:60 = x:4$

6. $5:x = 10:8$ $\qquad\qquad$ $x:15 = 2:1$ $\qquad\qquad$ $7:10 = 21:x$

Many proportion problems do not have whole number answers.

Example: Solve for c in $\dfrac{c}{3} = \dfrac{5}{7}$.

STEP 1.	Cross multiply. The cross product of c and 7 is $7 \times c$. The cross product of 3 and 5 is 15.	$\dfrac{c}{3} \bowtie \dfrac{5}{7}$
STEP 2.	To find c, divide 15 by the number in the incomplete cross product, 7. The value of c is $2\frac{1}{7}$.	$7 \times c = 15$ $c = 15 \div 7$ $c = 2\dfrac{1}{7}$

B. Solve each problem.

For problems 7 to 9, solve each proportion for the letter e.

7. $\dfrac{2}{3} = \dfrac{5}{e}$ $\qquad\qquad$ $\dfrac{7}{4} = \dfrac{e}{9}$ $\qquad\qquad$ $\dfrac{10}{e} = \dfrac{3}{8}$

8. $\dfrac{e}{15} = \dfrac{3}{4}$ $\qquad\qquad$ $\dfrac{9}{20} = \dfrac{4}{e}$ $\qquad\qquad$ $\dfrac{3}{2} = \dfrac{e}{5}$

9. $\dfrac{7}{10} = \dfrac{e}{5}$ $\qquad\qquad$ $\dfrac{e}{25} = \dfrac{5}{6}$ $\qquad\qquad$ $\dfrac{5}{8} = \dfrac{12}{e}$

For problems 10 and 11, rewrite each proportion with fractions. Then solve for the letter *d*.

10. 6:11 = 2:*d*   3:5 = *d*:8   16:*d* = 3:2

11. *d*:9 = 4:5   20:3 = 9:*d*   2:15 = *d*:4

For word problems, remember that the parts in a proportion must correspond to each other.

Example: A three-foot board weighs five pounds. What is the weight of an eight-foot board?

STEP 1.   Write a proportion of the ratio of feet (length) to pounds (weight). Use *w* for the weight of the 8-foot board.

$$\frac{\text{feet}}{\text{pounds}} \quad \frac{3}{5} = \frac{8}{w}$$

STEP 2.   Cross multiply. The cross product of 3 and *w* is $3 \times w$. The cross product of 5 and 8 is 40.

$$3 \times w = 40$$

STEP 3.   To find *w*, divide 40 by the number in the incomplete cross product, 3.

$$w = 40 \div 3$$
$$w = 13\frac{1}{3}$$

➡   The eight-foot board weighs $13\frac{1}{3}$ pounds.

C. Solve each problem.

12. The ratio of games won to games lost for the Eastport Eagles was 4:3. The team won 12 games. How many games did they lose?

13. An eight-acre field produced 280 bushels of wheat. At the same rate of production, how many bushels of wheat can be produced on 20 acres?

14. Sandra took a snapshot that was 4 inches wide and 5 inches long to be enlarged so that is was 20 inches long. If the width and length are in the same proportion as the original, how wide is the enlargement?

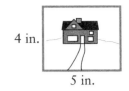

4 in.

5 in.

15. A bread recipe calls for 6 cups of flour and 4 tablespoons of butter. If Robert reduced the amount of flour to 4 cups, how much butter should he use?

16. Matt got eight hits in five baseball games. If he continues playing at this rate, how many hits should he get in 30 games?

17. Melva drove 144 miles in three hours. If she drives at the same rate, how far can she go in five hours?

18. According to a recipe a five-pound roast will serve six people. How big a roast is needed to serve nine people?

19. Joycelin paid $7.78 for two pounds of pork chops. What is the price for three pounds of pork chops?

20. For every $10 that the Chungs take home, they spend $3 on food for their family. What is their food bill for a week when they bring home $490?

21. The Islanders are winning 3 out of 4 games. If they continue playing at this rate, how many games will they have to play to win 12?

To check your answers, turn to page 104.

Ratios & Percents

Proportion Shortcuts

The factory where Raymond works produces plastic bottles. On an average, 3 out of every 200 bottles are defective. If the factory produces 2,400 bottles in a month, how many of them are defective?

Like many proportion problems, this one has rather large numbers. Instead of finding cross products and dividing, write out each cross product and cancel by the number in the incomplete cross product. Follow the example carefully.

Example: Find the number of defective bottles produced in a month at Raymond's factory.

STEP 1. Set up a proportion with ratios of defective bottles to total bottles produced.

$$\frac{\text{defective}}{\text{total}} \quad \frac{3}{200} = \frac{d}{2,400}$$

STEP 2. Write the cross products.

$$200 \times d = 3 \times 2,400$$

STEP 3. To solve for d, write 200 below the cross product $3 \times 2,400$. Then cancel.

$$d = \frac{3 \times \overset{12}{\cancel{2,400}}}{\underset{1}{\cancel{200}}}$$

$$d = 36$$

➡ Out of 2,400 bottles, 36 are defective.

Notice that the fraction bar below $3 \times 2,400$ acts as a division sign. You are dividing 200 into the cross product $3 \times 2,400$.

PRACTICE 7

Solve each proportion.

1. $\dfrac{20}{50} = \dfrac{m}{45}$ $\dfrac{32}{200} = \dfrac{48}{m}$ $\dfrac{500}{m} = \dfrac{300}{12}$

2. $\dfrac{15}{60} = \dfrac{45}{m}$ $\dfrac{m}{120} = \dfrac{18}{144}$ $\dfrac{20}{350} = \dfrac{16}{m}$

For problems 3 and 4, rewrite each proportion with fractions. Then solve.

3. $n{:}340 = 6{:}17$ $6{:}25 = n{:}750$ $30{:}80 = 24{:}n$

4. $300{:}n = 60{:}9$ $250{:}19 = 1{,}000{:}n$ $400{:}15 = n{:}90$

5. A plane flew 1,440 miles in 3 hours. At the same rate, how far can it fly in 5 hours?

6. Sharon paid $30.50 for 2 gallons of paint. What was the cost of 10 gallons of the same paint?

7. Each year there are about 5 divorces for every 1,000 people in the U.S. The population of Eastport is 13,000. If it follows the national pattern, how many divorces are there in one year in Eastport?

8. During a special sale, the ratio of customers using coupons to those paying full price was 2:5. There were 130 customers who paid full price. How many used coupons?

9. At Acme Tool, Co., 3 out of 20 workers got raises at their last review. Altogether there are 1,200 workers at Acme. How many of them got raises?

10. If a six-acre field produces 720 bushels of corn, how much corn can a farmer expect from a 48-acre field?

To check your answers, turn to page 107.

Ratios & Percents

Map Scales

Felipe is a truck driver. He has to pick up a load in the town of Rome shown on the map below and deliver the load in Athens. On the map, the distance between Rome and Athens is two inches. Find the distance in miles between the two towns.

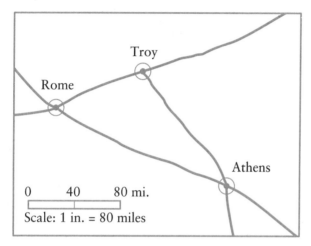

On most maps there is a *scale* that relates distance on the map (usually measured in inches or centimeters) to distance in the real world (usually measured in miles or kilometers). The scale is a ratio of map distance to actual distance. You can use the ratio to set up a proportion and solve for actual distance.

Example: What is the distance in miles between the towns of Rome and Athens?

STEP 1. Set up a proportion. The first ratio is the scale of the map, 1 inch = 80 miles. In the other ratio, write the distance in inches between the towns, 2. Use a letter to represent the actual distance.

$$\frac{\text{inches}}{\text{miles}} \quad \frac{1}{80} = \frac{2}{d}$$

STEP 2. Solve the proportion.

$$d = \frac{80 \times 2}{1}$$
$$d = 160 \text{ mi}$$

The distance between the towns is 160 miles.

PRACTICE 8

Solve each problem.

1. On the map on page 29, the distance between Rome and Troy is 1 inch. What is the distance in miles between the towns?

2. On the same map, the distance between Troy and Athens is $1\frac{1}{2}$ inches. Find the distance between Troy and Athens in miles. [**Hint:** You can use 1.5 for $1\frac{1}{2}$.]

3. The scale on the map of a large country is 1 inch = 200 miles. What is the distance in miles between two cities that are 3.5 inches apart on the map?

4. The scale on a regional map of Mexico is 1 centimeter = 20 kilometers. Find the distance in kilometers between two villages that are 1.75 centimeters apart on the map.

5. The distance between Albany and Buffalo is 300 miles. On a map with a scale of 1 inch = 25 miles, how many inches apart are Albany and Buffalo?

6. On a map of the U.S. the scale is 1 inch = 60 miles. St. Louis and Boston are approximately 20 inches apart on the map. What is the approximate distance in miles between St. Louis and Boston?

7. A detailed map of a city has a scale of 1 inch = 2,000 feet. What is the distance in feet between two museums that are $2\frac{1}{2}$ inches apart on the map? [**Hint:** You can use 2.5 for $2\frac{1}{2}$.]

8. On a map with a scale of 1 inch = 40 miles, Milwaukee and Omaha are 12.5 inches apart. Find the distance in miles between Milwaukee and Omaha.

To check your answers, turn to page 108.

Finding Unit Rates

Alex drove 324 miles on 12 gallons of gasoline. Find his gas mileage.

Gas mileage or miles per gallon is a ratio. It tells how far a vehicle moves with one gallon of gas. A *unit rate* is a ratio with a denominator of one. Miles per gallon, dollars per pound, points per game, and miles per hour are all examples of unit rates.

Proportion is a convenient tool for finding unit rates. When you find a unit rate, remember that the denominator for one of the ratios is always 1.

Example: Find the gas mileage for a 324-mile trip on 12 gallons of gasoline.

STEP 1. Set up a proportion. One ratio is miles driven to gallons used. In the other ratio, use a letter to represent the number of miles and 1 for the number of gallons.

$$\frac{\text{miles}}{\text{gallons}} \quad \frac{324}{12} = \frac{m}{1}$$

STEP 2. Solve the proportion.

$$m = \frac{324 \times 1}{12}$$
$$m = 27$$

⇒ Alex's gas mileage is 27 miles per gallon.

PRACTICE 9

Solve each of the following with a proportion.

1. Sandro drove his truck 252 miles on 18 gallons of gasoline. Find the number of miles he got per gallon of gas.

2. During a basketball season when he played 80 games, Dave Robinson scored 2,383 points. To the nearest whole number what were his points per game?

3. In Super Bowl XXIII Joe Montana completed 23 passes for 357 yards. To the nearest whole number find his yards per completion.

4. The Yoshimura family paid $38.25 for three theatre tickets. What was the price per ticket?

5. In the last ten years, the population of Eastport has grown by 4000. Find the population increase in people per year.

6. A restaurant charged $357.50 for thirteen people who attended a retirement party. What was the rate per person?

7. Mr. Moto makes $26,500 a year. Mrs. Moto makes $8,200 a year at her part-time job. They have three children at home, but none of the children has a job. What is the Moto family's per capita (per person) income? [**Hint:** First find their total yearly income.]

Use the following information to answer questions 8 to 11.

Silvia wants to compare the price of three shampoos. Brand X costs $3.99 for a 20-ounce bottle, Brand Y costs $2.69 for a 15-ounce bottle, and Brand Z costs $1.47 for a 6-ounce bottle.

To the nearest cent, find the price per ounce for:

8. Brand X.

9. Brand Y.

10. Brand Z.

11. Which shampoo is the best buy?

To check your answers, turn to page 108.

Multi-Step Proportions

The ratio of domestic cars to imported cars in Charlie's repair shop is 5:3. If there are 16 cars waiting to be served in Charlie's shop, how many of them are domestic?

For some proportion problems, you must find new ratios before setting up a proportion.

The number 16 is the actual number of cars in the shop, but neither number in the ratio 5:3 represents a total. The number 5 represents domestic cars, and 3 represents imported cars. Use these two numbers to find a number that represents the total.

Example: Find the number of domestic cars at Charlie's shop.

STEP 1. To get a number that represents a total, add the numbers in the ratio 5:3.

$$\begin{array}{r} 5 \text{ domestic} \\ + 3 \text{ imported} \\ \hline 8 \text{ total} \end{array}$$

STEP 2. Make a ratio of the number of domestic cars to the total number of cars.

$$\frac{\text{domestic}}{\text{total}} \quad \frac{5}{8}$$

STEP 3. Write and solve a proportion.

$$\frac{\text{domestic}}{\text{total}} \quad \frac{5}{8} = \frac{x}{16}$$

$$x = \frac{5 \times 16}{8}$$

$$x = 10$$

➡ There are 10 domestic cars in Charlie's shop.

Read each problem below carefully. Be sure the parts of the proportion correspond to the words in the question.

PRACTICE 10

Use a proportion to solve each problem. Some of the problems have hints to help you set up the right proportion.

1. The ratio of wins to losses for the Hawks basketball team was 3:1. If they played a total of 36 games, how many did they win? [**Hint:** Use the ratio to find the number of games they played.]

2. Bill used one gallon of white paint for every four gallons of yellow paint to make a mixture to paint his barn. If he used a total of 15 gallons of paint on the job, how many gallons were white?

3. Julissa has a job repairing office equipment. For every two days that she spends in the shop, she spends three days on the road making on-site repairs. In 20 work days, how many days does Julissa spend in the shop?

4. The ratio of problems correct to the total number of problems on Paul's last math quiz was 4:5. If there were 25 problems on the quiz, how many did Paul get *wrong*? [**Hint:** Use the numbers in the ratio to find a number that represents the problems Paul got wrong.]

5. For every $3 Maya spends on rent, she has $7 left over for other expenses. If she takes home $400 a week, how much of it goes for rent?

6. The ratio of students with work experience to the total number of students in John's boiler repair class is 1:9. There are 27 students in the class. How many of them have work experience?

7. The ratio of smokers to non-smokers in Malcolm's office is 1:5. Three people in the office are smokers. How many people work there?

8. At the factory where Carina works, the ratio of employees who walk to work to those who arrive by car is 2:19. Altogether there are 252 workers at the factory. How many of them walk to work?

9. The ratio of adults to children at ABC Daycare Center is 1:5. There are 60 children enrolled in the program. What is the total number of children and adults at the Daycare Center?

To check your answers, turn to page 109.

Proportion Review

The problems on these pages will help you decide if you need to review the proportion unit of this book. When you finish, look at the chart to see which pages you should review.

For problems 1 to 6, solve each proportion for the missing number (n).

1. $\dfrac{3}{8} = \dfrac{12}{n}$

2. $\dfrac{25}{6} = \dfrac{n}{4}$

3. $3:20 = n:150$

4. $\dfrac{5}{n} = \dfrac{2}{3}$

5. $\dfrac{n}{15} = \dfrac{1}{6}$

6. $n:9 = 7:30$

7. Gustavo drove 105 miles in two hours. Driving at the same rate, how far can he go in 7 hours?

8. The ratio of wins to losses for the Flyers is 3:2. So far they have won 9 games. How many have they lost?

9. The scale on a map is 1 inch = 60 miles. Two towns are 2.5 inches apart on the map. What is the distance between the towns in miles?

10. On a map of California the distance between Los Angeles and San Diego is 6.25 inches. The scale of the map is 1 inch = 20 miles. Find the distance between Los Angeles and San Diego in miles.

11. Martha paid $13.09 for a chunk of cheese that weighed 2.2 pounds. Find the price per pound of the cheese.

12. Isabella drove 319 miles on 11 gallons of gasoline. Find her gas mileage (miles per gallon) for the trip.

13. Mr. Pagan got 1,122 bushels of soybeans from 33 acres. Find the yield (bushels per acre) for the field of soybeans.

14. On a final exam, the ratio of the number of questions Carla got right to the number she missed was 5:1. There were 90 questions on the exam. How many did she get right?

15. In Mrs. Accardo's English as a second language class, the ratio of men to women is 3:5. There are 24 students in her class. How many of them are women?

16. At Brett's job he spends three hours typing for every two hours filing. During a 40-hour work week, how many hours does Brett type?

_____ PROGRESS CHECK _____

Check your answers on page 110. Then return to the review pages for the problems you missed. Correct your answers before going on to the next unit.

If you missed problems	Review pages
1 to 8	20 to 28
9 to 10	29 to 30
11 to 13	31 to 32
14 to 16	33 to 34

Understanding Percent

▼

What is a Percent?

Like a fraction or a decimal, a percent shows a part of a whole. Fractions divide a whole into 2 parts or 3 parts or 4 parts and so on. Decimals divide a whole into 10 parts or 100 parts or 1,000 parts and so on. The word *percent* means "out of 100." Percents divide a whole into 100 parts and only 100 parts. A percent is very much like a two-place decimal (hundredths).

The figure pictured here is divided into 100 parts, and 60 of the parts are shaded. The fraction $\frac{60}{100}$ which reduces to $\frac{3}{5}$ tells how much of the figure is shaded. The decimal .60 which simplifies to .6 also tells how much of the figure is shaded. 60% of the figure is shaded.

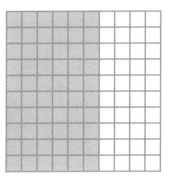

To work with percent, think of a whole as 100%.

Example: Maria spends 30% of her income for food for her family. What percent of her income is left for everything else?

100% represents Maria's total income.	100%
To find the amount that goes for everything besides food, subtract 30% from 100%.	− 30%
	70%

⟹ 70% of Maria's income is left for everything else.

PRACTICE 11

A. Answer each question.

1. On a snowy night, 40% of Ms. Ramos' students were late to class. What percent arrived on time?

2. The Smiths have paid off 80% of their car loan. What percent is left to pay?

3. Last year Stanley was absent only 1% of the time on his job. What percent of the time was he present?

4. The Hawks have won 66% of their ball games. What percent have they lost?

Remember that one whole is 100%. If something increases, it becomes more than 100% of itself.

Example: In the 5 years Livingston has worked at his job, his income has doubled. His income now is what percent of his income when he started?

Remember that one whole is 100%. $\qquad$ $2 \times 100\% = 200\%$
If something doubles, it becomes $2 \times 100\%$.

➡ Livingston's income is 200% of what it was 5 years ago.

B. Solve each problem.

5. The Garcias' house is worth four times the price they paid for it. The current value is what percent of the value when they bought the house?

6. The population of Midvale is ten times the population in 1950. The population now is what percent of the 1950 population?

To check your answers, turn to page 111.

Changing Decimals to Percents

To work with percent, you should be able to convert decimals, fractions, and percents to corresponding forms. The next four lessons explain how to interchange these forms.

It is easy to change decimals to percents. Move the decimal point two places to the **right** and write a percent sign.

Example: Change .25 to a percent.

STEP 1. Move the decimal point two places to the right.

STEP 2. Write a percent sign.

$.25 = .25 = 25\%$

When the decimal point moves to the end, you do not have to write the point.

Example: Change .043 to a percent.

STEP 1. Move the decimal point two places to the right.

STEP 2. Write a percent sign.

$.043 = .043 = 4.3\%$

Example: Change $.16\frac{2}{3}$ to a percent.

STEP 1. Move the decimal point two places to the right.

STEP 2. Write a percent sign.

$.16\frac{2}{3} = .16\frac{2}{3} = 16\frac{2}{3}\%$

When the decimal point comes just before a fraction, you do not have to write the point.

Sometimes you will have to put zeros after the decimal to get two places.

Example: Change .3 to a percent.

STEP 1. Put a zero at the right of .3.

STEP 2. Move the decimal point two places to the right.

STEP 3. Write a percent sign.

$.3 = .30 = 30\%$

Change each decimal to a percent.

1. .45 =   .08 =   .015 = $.66\frac{2}{3}$ =

2. .6 =   .15 = $.08\frac{1}{3}$ =   .96 =

3. .008 =   .4 =   .01 =   .5 =

4. 1.6 =   .24 =   .375 =   .9 =

5. 2.25 =   5. =   .02 = $.06\frac{2}{3}$ =   *To check your answers, turn to page 111.*

Changing Percents to Decimals

To change a percent to a decimal, move the decimal point two places to the **left** and take off the percent sign.

Example: Change 85% to a decimal.

Step 1.   Move the decimal point two places to the left.   85% = 85% = .85

Step 2.   Take off the percent sign.

Example: Change 3.9% to a decimal.

Step 1.   Put a zero to the left of 3.9%.   3.9% = 03.9% = .039   *Sometimes you need to add a zero at the left to get two places*

Step 2.   Move the decimal point two places to the left.

Step 3.   Take off the percent sign.

Example: Change 10% to a decimal.

STEP 1. Move the decimal point two places to the left.

STEP 2. Take off the percent sign.

$$10\% = \underset{\curvearrowleft}{10}\% = .10 = .1$$

Notice that we took off the zero at the right in .10. The zero does not change the value of .1.

Example: Change $22\frac{2}{9}\%$ to a decimal.

STEP 1. The decimal point is not written. It is understood to be at the right of 22. Move the decimal point two places to the left.

STEP 2. Take off the percent sign.

$$22\frac{2}{9}\% = \underset{\curvearrowleft}{22}\frac{2}{9}\% = .22\frac{2}{9}$$

PRACTICE 13

Change each percent to a decimal.

1. 15% =   6% =   62.5% =

2. 1% =   8.7% = $16\frac{2}{3}\%$ =

3. 40% =   125% =   60% =

4. 0.3% =   .5% =   1,000% =

5. $12\frac{1}{2}\%$ =   200% = $1\frac{1}{4}\%$ =

6. 6.3% =   17% =   48.4% =

7. 65% =   4.5% =   .2% =

To check your answers, turn to page 112.

Changing Fractions to Percents

There are two ways to change a fraction to a percent. Look at the examples on this page carefully. Then choose the method you like better.

One method for changing a fraction to a percent is to find a fraction of 100%. In other words, multiply the fraction by 100%.

Example: Change $\frac{3}{5}$ to a percent.

Multiply $\frac{3}{5}$ by 100%.

$$\frac{3}{5} \times 100\% = \frac{3}{\overset{1}{\cancel{5}}} \times \frac{\overset{20}{\cancel{100}}}{1} = \frac{60}{1} = 60\%$$

Example: Change $\frac{2}{7}$ to a percent.

Multiply $\frac{2}{7}$ by 100%.

$$\frac{2}{7} \times 100\% = \frac{2}{7} \times \frac{100}{1} = \frac{200}{7} = 28\frac{4}{7}\%$$

The other method for changing a fraction to a percent is to change the fraction to a decimal first. Then change the decimal to a percent.

Example: Change $\frac{1}{4}$ to a percent.

Step 1. Change $\frac{1}{4}$ to a decimal.

$$\frac{1}{4} = 4\overline{)1.00}^{\,.25}$$

Step 2. Change .25 to a percent.

$$.25 = .25 = 25\%$$

PRACTICE 14

Change each fraction to a percent.

1. $\frac{9}{10} =$ $\qquad$ $\frac{4}{5} =$ $\qquad$ $\frac{2}{9} =$ $\qquad$ $\frac{3}{50} =$

2. $\frac{4}{25} =$ $\qquad$ $\frac{1}{8} =$ $\qquad$ $\frac{2}{3} =$ $\qquad$ $\frac{1}{2} =$

3. $\frac{5}{6} =$ $\qquad$ $\frac{4}{7} =$ $\qquad$ $\frac{7}{100} =$ $\qquad$ $\frac{3}{8} =$

To check your answers, turn to page 112.

Changing Percents to Fractions

Remember that a percent is a kind of fraction. To change a percent to a fraction, write the digits in the percent as the numerator. Write 100 as the denominator. Then reduce the fraction.

Example: Change 65% to a fraction.

STEP 1.   Write 65 as the numerator. $\dfrac{65}{}$

STEP 2.   Write 100 as the denominator. $\dfrac{65}{100}$

STEP 3.   Reduce the fraction by 5. $\dfrac{65}{100} = \dfrac{65 \div 5}{100 \div 5} = \dfrac{13}{20}$

PRACTICE 15

A. Change each percent to a fraction and reduce.

1. 15% =   1% =   48% =   90% =

2. 22% =   8% =   125% =   4% =

3. 44% =   85% =   98% =   245% =

4. The Andersons put 12% of their income into a savings account. What fraction of their income do they put in the account?

5. Karl has written 90% of his term paper. What fraction of the paper has he written?

6. Last year, the Ruizes spent 20% of their income on rent. What fraction of their income did they spend on rent?

When a percent has a decimal in it, first change the percent to a decimal. Then change the decimal to a fraction.

Example: Change 4.8% to a fraction.

STEP 1.   Change 4.8% to a decimal. $4.8\% = 04.8 = .048$

STEP 2.   Change .048 to a fraction. $\dfrac{048}{1,000} = \dfrac{48 \div 8}{1,000 \div 8} = \dfrac{6}{125}$

STEP 3.   Reduce $\dfrac{48}{1,000}$ by 8.

B. Change each percent to a fraction and reduce.

7. 2.8% =   62.5% =   1.5% =   10.2% =

8. .05% =   11.5% =   87.5% =   1.25% =

9. Connie's employer withholds 12.5% of her pay for state income tax. What fraction of her pay is withheld?

10. In the last ten years the population of Midvale grew 8.5%. By what fraction did the population grow?

11. The unemployment rate for teenagers in Midvale is 16.4%. What fraction of the teenagers in Midvale are unemployed?

12. This year, all employees at T&R Associates will receive a 3.75% cost of living increase. What fraction of each employees current salary does the raise represent?

When a percent has a fraction in it, write the digits in the percent as the numerator. Write 100 as a denominator. Then **divide** the numerator by the denominator. This operation is complicated. Study the following example carefully.

Example: Change $41\frac{2}{3}\%$ to a fraction.

STEP 1. Write $41\frac{2}{3}$ as the numerator.

$$\frac{41\frac{2}{3}}{100}$$

STEP 2. Write 100 as the denominator.

STEP 3. Remember that the line separating the numerator from the denominator means "divided by." Divide $41\frac{2}{3}$ by 100.

$$41\frac{2}{3} \div 100 =$$

$$\frac{125}{3} \div \frac{100}{1} =$$

$$\frac{\overset{5}{\cancel{125}}}{3} \times \frac{1}{\underset{4}{\cancel{100}}} = \frac{5}{12}$$

To review dividing fractions, turn to New Basic Skills with Math: Fractions, *page 83.*

Study the next example carefully before you try the problems.

Example: Change $6\frac{2}{3}\%$ to a fraction.

STEP 1. Write $6\frac{2}{3}$ as the numerator.

$$\frac{6\frac{2}{3}}{100}$$

STEP 2. Write 100 as the denominator.

STEP 3. Divide $6\frac{2}{3}$ by 100.

$$6\frac{2}{3} \div 100 =$$

$$6\frac{2}{3} \div \frac{100}{1} =$$

$$\frac{\overset{1}{\cancel{20}}}{3} \times \frac{1}{\underset{5}{\cancel{100}}} = \frac{1}{15}$$

C. Change each percent to a fraction and reduce.

13. $16\frac{2}{3}\% =$ $37\frac{1}{2}\% =$ $8\frac{1}{3}\% =$ $6\frac{1}{4}\% =$

14. $88\frac{8}{9}\% =$ $83\frac{1}{3}\% =$ $57\frac{1}{7}\% =$ $4\frac{1}{6}\% =$

15. In Midvale, $66\frac{2}{3}\%$ of the residents own their homes. What fraction of the residents own their homes?

16. The interest rate on Mr. and Mrs. Santiago's mortgage is $8\frac{3}{4}$%. The interest rate is equal to what fraction?

17. Of the students in Mrs. Green's night school math class, $26\frac{2}{3}$% were born outside the U.S. What fraction of the students were born outside the U.S.?

To check your answers, turn to page 112.

Common Fractions, Decimals, and Percents

The exercise on this page will help you to learn some of the common fractions, decimals, and percents you will use most often in your work.

PRACTICE 16

Write an equivalent fraction and decimal for each percent. Then check your answers. Use the correct answers to fill in the chart on the next page. Study the answers carefully. Memorize the fraction and decimal that each percent is equal to.

1. 50%   25%   75% $12\frac{1}{2}$%

2. $37\frac{1}{2}$% $62\frac{1}{2}$% $87\frac{1}{2}$% $33\frac{1}{3}$%

3. $66\frac{2}{3}$%   20%   40%   60%

4. 80%   10%   30%   70%

5. 90% $16\frac{2}{3}$% $83\frac{1}{3}$%

To check your answers, turn to page 113.

Percent	Decimal	Fraction
50%	_____	_____
25%	_____	_____
75%	_____	_____
$12\frac{1}{2}\%$	_____	_____
$37\frac{1}{2}\%$	_____	_____
$62\frac{1}{2}\%$	_____	_____
$87\frac{1}{2}\%$	_____	_____
$33\frac{1}{3}\%$	_____	_____
$66\frac{2}{3}\%$	_____	_____
20%	_____	_____
40%	_____	_____
60%	_____	_____
80%	_____	_____
10%	_____	_____
30%	_____	_____
70%	_____	_____
90%	_____	_____
$16\frac{2}{3}\%$	_____	_____
$83\frac{1}{3}\%$	_____	_____

Identifying the Percent, the Whole, and the Part

Adrienne's employer calculated her new raise. 10% of her $450-a-week salary is $45.

Adrienne's situation is a typical percent problem. It has a percent, a whole, and a part.

$$10\% \times \$450 = \$45$$
$$\% \times \text{whole} = \text{part}$$

The **percent** is easy to identify. It has the % sign. The word *of* suggests multiplication. The word that follows *of* is usually the **whole.** (For Adrienne, the whole is her weekly salary.) The verb *is* suggests the = sign. The product of multiplying the percent times the whole is the **part.**

Example: Identify the percent, the whole, and the part in the statement: 6 is 20% of 30.

%	whole	part
20%	30	6

PRACTICE 17

A. For problems 1 to 6, fill in the blanks with the percent, the whole, and the part for each statement.

	%	whole	part
1. 25% of 36 is 9.	_____	_____	_____
2. 15 is 75% of 20.	_____	_____	_____
3. 12 is $33\frac{1}{3}\%$ of 36.	_____	_____	_____
4. 90% of 200 is 180.	_____	_____	_____
5. On a test with 40 problems, Carla got 80% right. She got 32 problems right.	_____	_____	_____
6. George paid Mike 50% of the $400 he borrowed. George has paid $200 so far.	_____	_____	_____

In a percent problem, one of the three elements is missing.

Example: Tell what is missing, the percent, the whole, or the part in:
10% of what number is 12?

Remember that the whole usually follows the word *of*. The whole is missing.

%	*whole*	*part*
10%	_____	12

Example: Tell what is missing, the percent, the whole, or the part in:
What is 5% of $120?

The percent is 5%, and the $120 following *of* is the whole. The part is missing.

%	*whole*	*part*
5%	$120	_____

B. For each problem, tell what is missing, the percent, the whole, or the part. Do not try to solve the problems.

7. Find $12\frac{1}{2}$% of 240.

8. 16 is what percent of 320?

9. What is 10.5% of 480?

10. 45 is 90% of what number?

11. What percent of 160 is 64?

12. 75% of what number is 33?

13. Find 2.5% of 6,000.

14. 12 is what percent of 2,000?

15. The Angelino family made a 15% deposit on a used car selling for $6,500. Find the amount of the deposit.

16. There are usually 24 students in Mrs. Rosado's math class. However, on the day before Thanksgiving, there were only 18 students in the class. What percent of the class was there?

17. Midvale spends 4% of its budget for health services. Last year's total budget was $3,500,000. How much did the town spend on health services last year?

18. Last year, 40,000 copies of the computer game *Satellite Warrior* were sold. This year, the software company sold only 25,000 copies of the game. This year's sales are what percent of last year's sales?

19. Eliza owes $200 on her credit cards. In one month, she has to pay a fee of 1.5% of the amount she owes. Find the amount of the fee on $200.

20. John spends $700 on rent each month. This is 30% of his monthly take-home pay. Find his monthly take-home pay.

21. Bowen Manufacturing has 420 employees. Of those, 105 work part time. What percent of the employees work part time?

To check your answers, turn to page 113.

Understanding Percent Review

The problems on these two pages will help you decide if you need to review this unit. Solve each problem. When you finish, look at the chart to see which pages you should review.

1. A rescue squad has raised 85% of the money they need to buy a new ambulance. What percent of the money do they still have to raise?

2. Bettina and Bill shared the driving on a trip. Bettina drove 60% of the total distance. What percent of the distance did Bill drive?

3. Melina now makes three times as much as she did when she started working 20 years ago. Her salary now is what percent of her salary 20 years ago?

For problems 4 to 6, change each decimal to a percent.

4. .25 =

5. .079 =

6. $.03\frac{1}{3}$ =

For problems 7 to 9, change each percent to a decimal.

7. 20% =

8. 6.25% =

9. 175% =

For problems 10 to 12, change each fraction to a percent.

10. $\frac{7}{20}$ =

11. $\frac{8}{9}$ =

12. $\frac{5}{6}$ =

For problems 13 to 15, change each percent to a fraction and reduce.

13. $16\% =$ **14.** $4.5\% =$ **15.** $2\frac{2}{3}\% =$

16. In the statement, 40% of 85 is 34, which number represents the part?

17. In the statement, 28.8 is 60% of 48, which number represents the whole?

18. Mario spends 30% of his monthly salary of $2,460 for rent. Does rent represent the percent, the whole, or the part?

PROGRESS CHECK

Check your answers on page 113. Then return to the review pages for the problems you missed. Correct your answers before going on to the next unit.

If you missed problems	Review pages
1 to 3	37 to 38
4 to 6	39
7 to 9	40 to 41
10 to 12	42
13 to 15	43 to 45
16 to 18	48 to 50

Finding
the Part

Finding the Part

Tom repairs and sells used cars and trucks. In June, 20% of the 45 vehicles he sold were trucks. How many trucks did he sell?

In the last lesson you learned that *percent × whole = part*. For Tom's truck sales, the percent is 20% and the whole is the 45 vehicles he sold in June.

To multiply by a percent, first change the percent to a decimal or a fraction. In this lesson you can practice both methods.

Example: Use a decimal to find 20% of 45.

STEP 1.   Change 20% to a decimal.

$$20\% = 20\% = .2$$

STEP 2.   Then multiply to find the part. Multiply 45 by .2.

$$\begin{array}{r} 45 \\ \times\ .2 \\ \hline 9.0 = 9 \end{array}$$

To review changing percents to decimals, turn to page 40.

▊▶   Tom sold 9 trucks in June.

PRACTICE 18

A. Use decimals to solve each problem.

1. 25% of 84 =   40% of 70 =   10% of 96 =

2. 15% of 80 =   24% of 200 =   19% of 300=

3. 80% of 15 =   5% of 120 =   90% of 80 =

4. 6% of 300 =   20% of 115 =   35% of 40 =

5. 12.5% of 64 =   8.5% of 700 =   1.2% of 1,000 =

6. 10.2% of 400 =   8.9% of 600 =   20.2% of 800 =

7. Mr. and Mrs. Soto make $28,500 a year. They spend 35% of their income on food. How much do the Sotos spend on food in a year?

8. The sales tax in Jeff's state is 6%. Jeff bought a jacket for $65. How much was the sales tax on the jacket?

9. There are 145,000 registered voters in Central County. At the last election 65% of the voters went to the polls. How many people voted in the county in the last election.

10. The Reeds are buying a house for $132,500. They have to make a down payment of 12%. How much is the down payment for the house?

You can also change the percent to a fraction to solve for the part.

Example: Use a fraction to find 20% of 45.

STEP 1. Change 20% to a fraction.

$$20\% = \frac{20}{100} = \frac{1}{5}$$

To review changing percents to fractions, turn to page 43.

STEP 2. Multiply 45 by $\frac{1}{5}$.

$$\frac{1}{\cancel{5}} \times \frac{\overset{9}{\cancel{45}}}{1} = \frac{9}{1} = 9$$

B. Use fractions to solve each problem.

11. 80% of 40 =   25% of 120 =   40% of 90 =

12. 60% of 75 =   75% of 64 =   50% of 48 =

13. 35% of 260 = $66\frac{2}{3}$% of 81 = $12\frac{1}{2}$% of 96 =

14. 90% of 340 = $62\frac{1}{2}$% of 320 = $83\frac{1}{3}$% of 72 =

15. 30% of 160 = $33\frac{1}{3}$% of 75 =   10% of 1,890 =

16. Anita's math test had 60 problems. She got 80% of them right. How many problems did she get right?

17. Adelle borrowed $4,500 to buy a car. So far she has paid back $33\frac{1}{3}$% of her loan. How much has she paid back?

18. A neighborhood association hopes to raise $2,500 to plant trees along their streets. So far they have raised 60% of the money. How much have they raised?

To check your answers, turn to page 114.

Using Proportion to Find the Part

The factory where Alex works makes plastic spools. Of the total spools produced at the factory, 12% are shipped outside the U.S. One month the factory produced 4,500 spools. How many were shipped outside the U.S.?

There is another way to solve percent problems. Set up a proportion using the model shown here. Then solve the proportion.

$$\frac{\text{part}}{\text{whole}} = \frac{\%}{100}$$

With a proportion, you do not need to change the percent to a decimal or to a fraction.

Example: Use a proportion to find 12% of 4,500.

STEP 1. Set up a proportion. 12 is the percent, and 4,500 is the whole. You are looking for the part. Use n for the part.

$$\frac{n}{4,500} = \frac{12}{100}$$

To review proportion shortcuts, turn to page 27.

STEP 2. Find the cross products and solve.

$$n = \frac{4,500 \times 12}{100}$$

$$n = 540$$

▏▶ 540 spools were shipped outside the U.S.

Note: There is no single right way to solve percent problems. Using proportion is simply an alternative. This lesson gives you a chance to practice using proportion.

PRACTICE 19

Use proportion to solve each problem.

1. 8% of 150 =   75% of 92 =   60% of 85 =

2. 37.5% of 56 =   8.5% of 600 =   14% of 400 =

3. 70% of 230 =   50% of 198 =   95% of 3,000 =

4. 20.2% of 1,600 =   1.5% of 900 =   20% of 160 =

5. 10% of 470 =   3% of 8,000 =   9.9% of 500 =

6. When Susana bought her car it was worth $12,000. Now it is worth only 35% of the original value. What is the value of the car now?

7. In a recent poll 1,500 people were interviewed. 55% of them approved of the President's domestic policies. How many of them approved?

8. A cordless drill that usually sells for $50 was on sale for 20% off. How much can you save by buying the drill on sale?

9. The Hawks have played 25 games and won 60% of them. How many games have they won?

10. There are 35 employees in Al's office. 80% of them are women. How many women work there?

11. Jake bought a used car for $1,800. He had to pay sales tax of 4.5%. Find the amount of the sales tax.

12. There are 220 beds in Memorial Hospital. Normally 85% of them are occupied. How many beds are normally occupied?

To check your answers, turn to page 114.

Rounding Money

Angela bought a pair of wool socks for $4.49. She had to pay 8% sales tax on the socks. Find the amount of tax.

The answers to many percent problems need to be "rounded off." Some answers have too many decimal places.

Example: Find 8% of $4.49.

STEP 1. Change 8% to a decimal.

$$8\% = 08\% = .08$$

STEP 2. Multiply $4.49 by .08.

$$
\begin{array}{r}
\$4.49 \\
\times\quad .08 \\
\hline
\$.3592
\end{array}
$$

The answer $.3592 has too many decimal places. Money has only two decimal places. Dimes are in the first, or tenths, place. Pennies are in the second, or hundredths, place. Answers to money problems should have no more than two places.

To round off an answer to the nearest cent, look at the digit in the thousandths (third) decimal place.

If the digit in the thousandths place is more than 4, add 1 to the cents (hundredths).

If the digit in the thousandths place is less than 5, leave the cents alone.

Example: Round $.3592 to the nearest cent.

STEP 1. Look at the digit in the thousandths place.

$$\$.3592$$

STEP 2. Since 9 is in the thousandths place, add 1 to the cents.

$.3592 to the nearest cent is $.36.

➠ The tax on the socks is $.36.

To review rounding, turn to New Basic Skills with Math: Decimals, *pages 17–19.*

PRACTICE 20

Use decimals or proportion to solve each problem. Round off each answer to the nearest cent.

1. 6% of $5.49 =   8% of $2.55 =   5% of $16.33 =

2. 9% of $8.25 =   12% of $9.89 =   15% of $25.44 =

3. 10% of $2.37 =   2% of $4.52 =   14% of $36.70 =

4. 4% of $8.12 =   13% of $25.50 =   3% of $31.60 =

5. 3.7% of $24.60 =   2.2% of $14.90 =   4.3% of $85 =

6. Sam paid 6.5% tax on an electric sander that cost $46.90. Find the amount of the tax.

7. Celeste bought a shirt for $24.85. Find the sales tax if the tax rate in her state is 7%.

8. Nikos paid a 1.5% finance charge on a $723 credit card balance. Find the amount of the charge.

9. At a sales tax rate of 4.5%, what is the tax on a sweatshirt that costs $19.80?

10. Maxine paid 5% down on a new computer system. The cost of the system was $1,895.90. Find the amount of her down payment.

To check your answers, turn to page 114.

Less than 1%

Of the plastic that is thrown out at the factory where Marco works, only .4% is recycled. If the factory throws out 1,200 pounds of plastic refuse each year, what is the weight of the plastic that gets recycled?

Remember that 1% is only 1 out of the 100 parts in a whole. In problems that ask for less than 1%, the part will be much smaller than the whole.

Example: Find .4% of 1,200.

STEP 1.	Change .4% to a decimal.	.4% = 00.4% = .004
STEP 2.	Multiply 1,200 by .004.	$\begin{array}{r} 1,200 \\ \times\ \ .004 \\ \hline 4.800 = 4.8 \end{array}$

➠ The factory recycles only 4.8 pounds of plastic a year.

PRACTICE 21

Use decimals or proportion to solve each problem.

1. .2% of 620 =   .8% of 70 =   .25% of 960 =

2. .5% of 450 =   .3% of 2,000 =   .9% of 2,100 =

3. .75% of $400 =   .1% of $395 =   .6% of $840 =

4. The yearly public works budget for the town of Midvale is $265,000. Of this amount .5% goes for new landscaping. What is the yearly budget for new landscaping?

5. In a recent year there were about 22,000,000 people living in the U.S. who were born outside the country. Of these .4% were born in Brazil. How many people born in Brazil were living in the U.S. that year?

To check your answers, turn to page 115.

More than 100%

When she started working three years ago, Natalie made $12 an hour. Her wage now is 150% of her starting wage. Find her wage now.

Remember that 100% is 1 whole. In problems where the percent is greater than 100%, the "part" will actually be more than the "whole."

Example: Find 150% of $12.

STEP 1.   Change 150% to a fraction.

$$150\% = \frac{150}{100} = \frac{3}{2}$$

STEP 2.   Multiply $12 by $\frac{3}{2}$.

$$\frac{3}{\underset{1}{2}} \times \frac{\overset{6}{\$12}}{1} = \frac{\$18}{1} = \$18$$

⇒   Natalie now makes $18 an hour.

PRACTICE 22

Use fractions or proportion to solve each problem.

1. 125% of 60 =   230% of 400 =   110% of 70 =

2. 400% of 18 =   175% of 640 =   340% of 65 =

3. 250% of $40 =   1,000% of $16 =   120% of $3.40 =

4. In 1960 there were 12,800 children in the Midvale school system. The number of students now is 140% of the number in 1960. How many children are in Midvale schools now?

5. In 1960 there were 88 men teaching in the Midvale school system. The number of men teaching now is 175% of the number in 1960. How many men teach in the Midvale schools now?

To check your answers, turn to page 115.

Quick Answers

Candido makes $430 a week, and he hopes to get a 10% raise. How much more will he make each week?

Finding 10% of a number is an example of one of several easy to calculate percent problems. Since $10\% = \frac{1}{10}$, you can find 10% of a number simply by dividing by 10. Study the list below:

To find 50%, divide by 2.	Why?	Because $50\% = \frac{1}{2}$
To find $33\frac{1}{3}\%$, divide by 3.		Because $33\frac{1}{3}\% = \frac{1}{3}$
To find 25%, divide by 4.		Because $25\% = \frac{1}{4}$
To find 20%, divide by 5.		Because $20\% = \frac{1}{5}$
To find 10%, divide by 10.		Because $10\% = \frac{1}{10}$

Example: What is 10% of $430?

Divide $430 by 10. $430 \div 10 = 43$.

➡ Candido will get $43 more each week.

PRACTICE 23

Use the shortcuts listed above to solve each problem.

1. 50% of 84 =   25% of 36 =   20% of 45 =

2. $33\frac{1}{3}\%$ of 60 =   10% of 390 =   50% of 1,600 =

3. 25% of $240 = $33\frac{1}{3}\%$ of $90 =   20% of $6.50 =

4. 10% of $5.30 =   50% of $112 =   25% of $500 =

5. John has to read a 486-page book for his English class. He has read 50% of the book. How many pages has he read?

6. Charlene owes $960 on her credit card. She pays 25% of the bill. How much did she pay?

To check your answers, turn to page 115.

Using Circle Graphs

A **circle graph** shows parts of a whole. Often each pie-shaped piece represents a percent. The sum of the pieces is 100%.

The circle graph pictured here shows how farmland in Central County is used.

Farmland Use

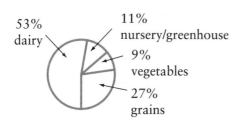

53% dairy

11% nursery/greenhouse

9% vegetables

27% grains

Example: What percent of the farmland is used for dairy?

According to the graph, 53% of the farmland is for dairy.

Example: The total acres of farmland in Central County is 30,000. About how many acres of Central County is used for grain production?

STEP 1. Find the section labeled "grains" on the graph. Grains are 27%.

STEP 2. Find 27% of 30,000.
$$27\% = 27\% = .27$$
$$.27 \times 30,000 = 8,100$$

8,100 acres in Central County are used for grain production.

Use the following circle graph to answer questions 1 to 7.

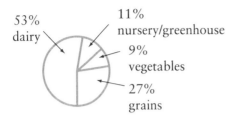

Farmland Use

53%
dairy

11%
nursery/greenhouse

9%
vegetables

27%
grains

1. According to the graph, what percent of Central County farmland is used for vegetable production?

2. According to the graph, what percent of Central County farmland is for nursery/greenhouse use?

3. Of the 30,000 acres of farmland in Central County, how many acres are for nursery/greenhouse use?

4. Of the 30,000 acres of farmland in Central County, how many acres are used for dairy?

5. West County has the same farm use as Central County. The area of farmland in West County is 42,000 acres. How many acres in West County are used for vegetable production?

6. Based on the graph, what is the total percent of farmland *not* used to grow vegetables and grains?

7. Of the 42,000 acres of farmland in West County, how many acres are used for nursery/greenhouse production?

This graph tells the way Americans spend their incomes. Use the graph to answer questions 8–12.

How Americans Spend

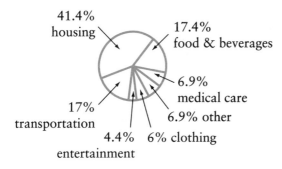

8. The Malevsky family follows the national spending pattern. Their monthly income is $2,300. How much do they spend in a typical month for food and beverages?

9. The combined income of the Rodriguez family is $3,150 a month. If they follow the national pattern, how much do they spend each month on clothing?

10. Anya makes $460 a week. If she spends at the national average, how much does she spend on transportation each week?

11. In a year the Kazakis family makes $31,200. If their expenses follow the national pattern, how much do they spend for medical care?

12. Fred follows the national spending pattern. He tries to put all of the category labeled "other" into savings. If he makes $2,200 a month, how much does he save each month?

To check your answers, turn to page 115.

Interest

Fran borrowed $400 from her brother for one year. She agreed to pay him 8% annual interest on the loan. How much will she pay in interest on the loan?

Interest is money someone pays for using someone else's money. A bank pays you interest for using your money in a savings account. You pay a bank interest for using the bank's money on a loan.

To find interest, multiply the principal by the rate and by the time.

> The formula for finding interest is $i = p \times r \times t$ where p is the **principal**—the money you borrow or save, r is the **rate**—the percent of interest, and t is the **time**—the number of years.

Example: Find the interest on $400 at 8% annual interest for one year.

STEP 1. Change 8% to a fraction.

$$8\% = \frac{8}{100}$$

STEP 2. Multiply the principal by the rate and by the time.

$$\frac{\overset{4}{\cancel{400}}}{1} \times \frac{8}{\underset{1}{\cancel{100}}} \times 1 = \$32$$

➡ Fran will pay $32 in interest.

Example: Find the interest on $2,000 at 6.5% annual interest for one year.

STEP 1. Change 6.5% to a decimal.

$$6.5\% = 06.5\% = .065$$

STEP 2. Multiply the principal by the rate and by the time.

When the time is one year, you do not have to multiply by 1.

$$\begin{array}{r} \$2000 \\ \times \quad .065 \\ \hline 10\ 000 \\ 120\ 00 \\ \hline \$130.000 \end{array}$$

➡ The interest is $130.00.

PRACTICE 25

A. Find the interest for each of the following.

1. $500 at 6% annual interest for one year.

2. $1,000 at 12% annual interest for one year.

3. $1,200 at $5\frac{1}{2}$% annual interest for one year.

4. $700 at 4.8% annual interest for one year.

5. $3,000 at 12.5% annual interest for one year.

6. $650 at 4.5% annual interest for one year.

7. $800 at $5\frac{3}{4}$% annual interest for one year.

When the time period for interest is not one year, change the time to a fraction of a year.

Example: Find the interest on $500 at 8% annual interest for 9 months.

STEP 1. Change 8% to a fraction. $\qquad 8\% = \dfrac{8}{100}$

STEP 2. Change 9 months to a fraction. Write 9 in the numerator and 12 months (one whole year) in the denominator. $\qquad \dfrac{9}{12} = \dfrac{3}{4}$

STEP 3. Multiply the principal by the rate and by the time.

$$\dfrac{\overset{5}{\cancel{500}}}{1} \times \dfrac{\overset{2}{\cancel{8}}}{\underset{1}{\cancel{100}}} \times \dfrac{3}{\underset{1}{\cancel{4}}} = \$30$$

➠ The interest is $30.

Example: Find the interest on $900 at 15% annual interest for one year and 8 months.

STEP 1. Change 15% to a fraction.

$$15\% = \frac{15}{100}$$

STEP 2. Change 1 year and 8 months to a mixed number. Write 1 year as a whole number. Write 8 months as a fraction over 12 months.

$$1\frac{8}{12} = 1\frac{2}{3} = \frac{5}{3}$$

STEP 3. Multiply the principal by the rate and by the time.

$$\frac{\overset{9}{900}}{1} \times \frac{\overset{5}{15}}{\underset{1}{100}} \times \frac{5}{\underset{1}{3}} = \$225$$

⟹ The interest is $225.

B. Find the interest for each of the following.

8. $600 at 4% annual interest for 6 months.

9. $2,000 at 8% annual interest for 3 months.

10. $1,200 at 7% annual interest for 5 months.

11. $250 at 6% annual interest for 1 year and 4 months.

12. $1,000 at 9% annual interest for 2 years and 6 months.

13. $1,800 at $4\frac{1}{2}$% annual interest for 10 months.

14. $1,500 at 12% annual interest for 1 year and 6 months.

15. $600 at 1.5% annual interest for 1 year 9 months.

To check your answers, turn to page 116.

Multi-Step Problems

In many percent problems, you will use two operations to find the answer. Sometimes you will first find a percent of a number. Then you will add this new amount to an old amount in the problem.

Example: George bought a used car for $1,600. He fixed the car and sold it for 25% more than he paid for it. How much did George sell the car for?

STEP 1.   Change 25% to a fraction.

$$25\% = \frac{25}{100} = \frac{1}{4}$$

STEP 2.   Multiply $1,600 by $\frac{1}{4}$.

$$\frac{1}{4} \times \$1,600 = \frac{1}{\underset{1}{4}} \times \frac{\overset{400}{\cancel{1,600}}}{1} = \$400$$

STEP 3.   Add $400 to $1,600.

$$\begin{array}{r} \$1,600 \\ +\quad 400 \\ \hline \$2,000 \end{array}$$

➠   George sold the car for $2,000.

Sometimes you will need to first find the percent of a number. Then you will subtract this new amount from an old amount in the problem.

Example: Jane bought a coat on sale. The coat used to cost $49. She bought it for 15% off the old price. How much did Jane pay for the coat?

STEP 1.   Change 15% to a decimal.

$$15\% = 15\% = .15$$

STEP 2.   Multiply $49 by .15.

$$\begin{array}{r} \$49 \\ \times\quad .15 \\ \hline 2\ 45 \\ 4\ 9\quad \\ \hline \$7.35 \end{array}$$

STEP 3.   Subtract $7.35 from $49.

$$\begin{array}{r} \$49.00 \\ -\quad 7.35 \\ \hline \$41.65 \end{array}$$

➠   Jane paid $41.65 for the coat.

Read each problem carefully, then solve. Round off money answers to the nearest cent.

1. Last year Manny made $22,350 a year. This year he got a 9% raise. How much will Manny make this year?

2. Gordon bought a shirt for $19.85. The sales tax in Gordon's state is 6%. What was the price of the shirt, including the sales tax?

3. Naomi makes $424 a week. Her employer takes out 18% of her pay for taxes and social security. How much does Naomi take home each week?

4. In 1970 the Canadian dollar was worth $.92 in U.S. money. In 1995 the Canadian dollar was worth 20% less than in 1970. What was the value of the Canadian dollar in 1995?

5. Lois took a test with 80 questions. She answered 90% of the questions correctly. How many questions did she get wrong?

6. In 1960 there were 24 women working at the Apex Canning Company. In 1995 there were 250% more women at Apex than in 1960. How many women worked at Apex in 1995?

7. A year ago Frank weighed 220 pounds. He went on a diet and lost 15% of his weight. How much did Frank weigh at the end of his diet?

8. Susan bought a clock for $24.49. The sales tax in Susan's state is 8%. How much did she pay for the clock, including the sales tax?

9. There are 840 children enrolled at the Oakdale School. The day of a snowstorm, 25% of the children were absent. How many children went to school on the day of the storm?

10. In the summer it costs about 24¢ a day to run a refrigerator. In the winter it costs $16\frac{2}{3}$% less than in the summer. How much does it cost to run a refrigerator on a winter day?

11. In 1985 the U.S. government spent about $250 billion on defense. In 1993 the government spent about 16% more on defense than in 1985. About how much did the U.S. spend in 1993 on defense?

12. Leah bought a saw on sale. The original price was $24.90. Leah bought the saw for 20% off the old price. How much did Leah pay for the saw?

13. Bill and Heather bought a house for $132,500. They made a down payment of 12%. Find the amount they owed on the house after they made the down payment.

14. A year ago Alice paid $.89 for a quart of milk. This year she pays 20% more than last year. How much does Alice pay for a quart of milk this year?

15. Je Chan works construction. He worked 210 days in 1994. In 1995, he worked 10% more days than in 1994. How many days did he work in 1995?

16. Four years ago, America and Omar bought a new car for $12,800. Recently, they sold it for 35% less than they paid for it new. What amount did they sell the car for?

To check your answers, turn to page 116.

Finding the Part Review

The problems on these two pages will help you decide if you need to review this unit. Solve each problem. When you finish, look at the chart to see which pages you should review.

1. 35% of 90 =

2. 80% of 115 =

3. 7.5% of 600 =

4. $12\frac{1}{2}$% of 240 =

5. 40% of 45 =

6. $33\frac{1}{3}$% of 63 =

7. Sam put 8% down on a used motorcycle selling for $1,500. How much was his down payment?

8. In the Westbrook neighborhood, 90% of the households send their children to local public schools. There are 840 families with children in Westbrook. How many of the families send their children to public schools?

For problems 9 and 10, round each answer to the nearest cent.

9. Find 6.5% of $12.95.

10. What is 3% of $6.48?

11. Find .4% of 650.

12. What is .75% of 900?

13. Find 120% of 460.

14. What is 450% of 2,000?

The circle graph shows the marital status of adults in the U.S. Use the graph to answer questions 15 to 17.

Adult Marital Status

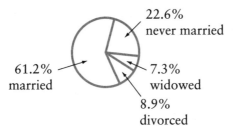

22.6%
never married

61.2%
married

7.3%
widowed

8.9%
divorced

15. What percent of adults in the U.S. are divorced?

16. There are approximately 27,000 adults in the town of Westlake. If West-lake follows the national pattern, how many of them are married?

17. The town of Northport has about 12,000 adults. If it follows the national trend, how many adults in Northport were never married?

18. Find the interest on $930 at 8% annual interest for one year.

19. What is the interest on $600 at 18.5% annual interest for three months?

20. Elena bought a $149 lawn mower on sale for "25% off." What was the sale price of the mower?

21. Phil bought a leather jacket for $169. The sales tax in his state is 7.5%. What was the price of the jacket including sales tax?

Check your answers on page 118. Then return to the review pages for the problems you missed. Correct your answers before going on to the next unit.

If you missed problems	*Review pages*
1 to 8	53 to 57
9 to 10	58 to 59
11 to 12	60
13 to 14	61
15 to 17	63 to 65
18 to 19	66 to 68
20 to 21	69 to 70

UNIT 5

Finding the Percent and the Whole

Finding What Percent One Number Is of Another

There are 48 employees at Pro Printers. Of these employees, 12 work part-time. What percent of the employees work part-time?

When you studied fractions, you learned how to find what part one number is of another. You made a fraction with the part as the numerator (top number) and the whole as the denominator (bottom number). The steps are the same for finding what percent one number is of another. Make a fraction with the part over the whole. Then change the fraction to a percent.

Example: 12 is what percent of 48?

STEP 1. Make a fraction with the part, 12, over the whole, 48, and reduce. $\frac{\text{part}}{\text{whole}}\ \frac{12}{48} = \frac{1}{4}$

STEP 2. Change $\frac{1}{4}$ to a percent. $\frac{1}{\cancel{4}_1} \times \frac{\cancel{100\%}^{25}}{1} = \frac{25}{1} = 25\%$

To review changing fractions to percents, turn to page 42.

➡ 25% of the employees at Pro Printers work part-time.

PRACTICE 27

A. Solve each problem.

1. 15 is what percent of 75?   What percent of 27 is 18?

2. What percent of 35 is 21?   36 is what percent of 48?

3. 64 is what percent of 128?   24 is what percent of 60?

4. What percent of 50 is 35?   18 is what percent of 48?

5. 240 is what percent of 300?   45 is what percent of 54?

6. The Alonsos make $1,840 a month. They spend $460 a month for rent. What percent of their income do the Alonsos spend on rent?

7. Last year Silvia weighed 160 pounds. She went on a diet and lost 20 pounds. What percent of her weight did she lose?

8. There are 350 people who work at the Allied Paper Products factory. Of these workers 280 are members of a union. What percent of the workers are union members?

9. Last year Cecilia paid $1.80 for a loaf of bread. This year the same brand of bread costs $.36 more. The increase is what percent of last year's price?

10. Kareem borrowed $1,200. When he paid his loan, he paid $72 interest. The interest was what percent of the loan?

In the last problems you compared a small number to a larger one. Sometimes you must compare a large number to a smaller number.

Example: 30 is what percent of 24?

STEP 1.   Remember that the whole usually follows the word *of*. In this problem the part, 30, is larger than the whole. Make a fraction with the part over the whole and reduce.

$$\frac{part}{whole}\ \ \frac{30}{24} = \frac{5}{4}$$

STEP 2.   Change $\frac{5}{4}$ to a percent.

$$\frac{5}{4} \times \frac{\overset{25}{\cancel{100\%}}}{1} = \frac{125}{1} = 125\%$$

➔   30 is 125% of 24.

Since 30 is more than 24, it is more than 100% of 24.

B. Solve each problem.

11. 100 is what percent of 80?   40 is what percent of 16?

12. What percent of 90 is 150?   66 is what percent of 48?

13. 165 is what percent of 75?   What percent of 35 is 105?

14. 19 is what percent of 19?   What percent of 42 is 84?

15. 75 is what percent of 25?   450 is what percent of 200?

16. Ten years ago there were 25,000 people in Southport. Now there are 35,000. The population now is what percent of the population ten years ago?

17. Paula started working at a drugstore for $8 an hour. Now that she is a manager, she makes $15 an hour. Her wage now is what percent of her wage when she started?

18. In 1990 Max's Music sold about 3,000 CDs. In 1995 the store sold almost 9,000 CDs. The 1995 sales were what percent of the 1990 sales?

19. In 1970 an ounce of gold was worth $35. In 1995 an ounce of gold was worth $385. The 1995 value was what percent of the 1970 value?

20. On her driver's test, Eunsook answered 22 questions correctly. There were 25 questions on the test. What percent of the questions did she answer correctly?

21. Stuart earned $1,800 last month selling newspaper advertising. At the end of the month, his boss gave him a $90 bonus. What percent of his monthly earnings was the bonus?

22. Frida estimated that her family's holiday dinner would cost $130. The actual cost was $127.40. What percent of the estimate was the actual cost of the dinner?

23. At Manny's Service Station, the usual cost of an oil change is $28. This Thursday, the cost will be only $21. What percent of the usual cost is the reduced cost?

To check your answers, turn to page 118.

Using Proportion to Find the Percent

David works as a printer. During a typical 40-hour work week, he spends 24 hours maintaining equipment. What percent of his time does he spend maintaining equipment?

Proportion is a convenient way to set up percent problems. Use the model shown here.

$$\frac{\text{part}}{\text{whole}} = \frac{\%}{100}$$

Example: Use proportion to solve the problem, 24 is what percent of 40?

STEP 1. Set up a proportion. 24 is the part, and 40 is the whole. You are looking for the percent. Use p for the percent.

$$\frac{24}{40} = \frac{p}{100}$$

To review proportion shortcuts, turn to page 27.

STEP 2. Find the cross products and solve.

$$p = \frac{\overset{12}{\cancel{24}} \times \overset{5}{\cancel{100}}}{\underset{\underset{1}{2}}{\cancel{40}}}$$

$$p = 60\%$$

⟹ David spends 60% of his time maintaining equipment.

Note: There is no single right way to solve percent problems. Proportion is simply an alternative. This lesson gives you a chance to practice using proportion.

PRACTICE 28

Use proportion to solve each problem.

1. 14 is what percent of 70?   What percent of 80 is 25?

2. 90 is what percent of 120?   140 is what percent of 400?

3. What percent of 150 is 15?   80 is what percent of 160?

Using Proportion to Find the Percent ——————————————— **79**

4. 135 is what percent of 150?   280 is what percent of 320?

5. 45 is what percent of 500?   What percent of 200 is 25?

6. What percent of 75 is 9?   150 is what percent of 60?

7. Walt took a test with 120 problems. He got 102 problems right. What percent of the problems did Walt get right?

8. Jaime borrowed $2,000. He had to pay $240 interest on the amount he borrowed. The interest was what percent of the loan?

9. There are eighteen students in Mr. Hoffman's night school math class. One evening six students were absent. What percent of the students were absent?

10. Alfonso works 40 hours a week. He spends about 15 hours every week typing. What percent of his work week does he spend typing?

11. Naomi wants to save $3,200 for a motorcycle. So far she has saved $2,000. What percent of the price has she saved?

12. The Bluebirds played 80 games and won 68 of them. What percent of the games did they win?

13. The Chan's house is now valued at $140,000. In the early 1970s they bought the house for $50,000. The value now is what percent of the price they paid?

To check your answers, turn to page 119.

Percent of Increase

In 1985 Jed made $360 a week. In 1995 he made $450 a week. By what percent did Jed's income increase from 1985 to 1995?

In some problems you must compare the difference between two amounts to an original amount. In this example, first find out how much more Jed makes now. Then compare the difference (the increase) to the amount he made in 1985 (the original amount).

Example: What is the percent of increase from $360 to $450?

STEP 1. Find the amount of increase. Subtract $360 from $450.

$$\begin{array}{r} \$450 \\ -\ \$360 \\ \hline \$90 \end{array}$$

STEP 2. Make a fraction with the increase, $90, over the original amount.

$$\frac{\text{increase}}{\text{original}}\ \frac{\$90}{\$360} = \frac{1}{4}$$

STEP 3. Change $\frac{1}{4}$ to a percent.

$$\frac{1}{\cancel{4}_{1}} \times \frac{\overset{25}{\cancel{100}}\%}{1} = \frac{25}{1} = 25\%$$

➟ Jed's income increased by 25%.

You can also solve this problem with a proportion by using the increase as the part and the original as the whole.

$$\frac{\text{increase}}{\text{original}}\ \frac{\$90}{\$360} = \frac{p}{100}$$

$$p = \frac{\overset{1}{\cancel{90}} \times \overset{25}{\cancel{100}}}{\underset{\underset{1}{\cancel{4}}}{\cancel{360}}}$$

$$p = 25\%$$

PRACTICE 29

Solve each problem.

1. Find the percent of increase from 24 to 36.

2. By what percent does 35 increase to 40?

3. What is the percent of increase from 60 to 96?

4. From 63 to 84 is what percent of increase?

5. What is the percent of increase from 120 to 228?

6. Find the percent of increase from $380 to $418.

7. Last year 16 houses sold in the Westbrook subdivision. This year 20 houses sold. By what percent did the number of sold houses increase?

8. Last year Celeste's rent was $450 a month. This year she pays $486. By what percent did her rent increase?

9. In 1970 there were 240,000 people living in Eastlake County. In 1995 there were 330,000 people. By what percent did the population increase from 1970 to 1995.

10. The Tenth Street Tenants' Association started with 18 members. In six months there were 63 members. By what percent did the membership increase in six months?

11. Don manages a music shop. He pays his suppliers $6.20 for each cassette. He charges customers $8.68 for a cassette. By what percent does Don mark up the price?

12. Last year a bus ride cost $1.25. This year a bus ride costs $1.50. By what percent did the price increase?

To check your answers, turn to page 119.

Percent of Decrease

Beatrice bought an electric fan on sale for $40. Before the sale, the fan cost $50. Find the discount rate on the original price.

A discount rate is a percent of decrease. First find the amount of the decrease (the discount). Then compare the decrease to the original amount.

Example: What is the percent of decrease from $50 to $40.

STEP 1. Find the amount of decrease (the discount). Subtract $40 from $50.

$$\begin{array}{r} \$50 \\ -\ \ 40 \\ \hline \$10 \end{array}$$

STEP 2. Make a fraction with the decrease, $10, over the original amount.

$$\frac{\text{decrease}}{\text{original}}\ \ \frac{\$10}{\$50} = \frac{1}{5}$$

STEP 3. Change $\frac{1}{5}$ to a percent.

$$\frac{1}{\cancel{5}_{1}} \times \frac{\overset{20}{\cancel{100\%}}}{1} = \frac{20}{1} = 20\%$$

⇒ The discount rate was 20%.

You can also solve this problem with a proportion by using the decrease as the part and the original as the whole.

$$\frac{\text{decrease}}{\text{original}}\ \ \frac{\$10}{\$50} = \frac{p}{100}$$

$$p = \frac{10 \times \overset{2}{\cancel{100}}}{\underset{1}{\cancel{50}}}$$

$$p = 20\%$$

PRACTICE 30

Solve each problem.

1. Find the percent of decrease from 80 to 60.

2. By what percent does 90 decrease to 81?

3. What is the percent of decrease from 200 to 120?

4. From 320 to 80 is what percent of decrease?

5. What is the percent of decrease from $840 to $560?

6. Find the percent of decrease from $1,200 to $1,140.

7. Last year there were 20 members of the Eastlake Rescue Squad. This year there are only 11. By what percent did the number of members decrease?

8. Carlos bought a calculator on sale. Before the sale the calculator cost $24. The sale price was $16. Find the rate of discount on the original price.

9. Last term 132 students signed up for night school at the Midvale Community Center. This year only 120 students signed up. By what percent did the number of school students decrease?

10. A waterproof jacket regularly sells for $150. A local department store has the jacket on sale for $132. Find the percent of discount on the jacket.

11. Two years ago there were 128 fires reported in Midvale. Last year there were only 96 reported fires. By what percent did the number of reported fires drop?

12. After an illness Mary decided to work only part-time. Her weekly pay dropped from $620 a week to $434. By what percent did her pay drop?

To check your answers, turn to page 120.

Finding a Number When a Percent of It Is Given

There are 21 salespeople working at the Carter Supply Company. Salespeople are 30% of the total number of employees. How many employees work at Carter Supply?

When you studied fractions, you learned how to find a whole when a part of the whole was given. These problems are a kind of "backwards multiplication." To find the missing number, you must divide by the fraction.

The steps are the same for finding a whole when a percent of it is given. Change the percent to a fraction or a decimal. Then divide the part by the fraction or decimal. When you go on to study algebra, you will often use this method to solve problems. It is called using *opposite operations*.

Example: 30% of what number is 21?

Using a fraction:

STEP 1.   Change 30% to a fraction.

$$30\% = \frac{30}{100} = \frac{3}{10}$$

STEP 2.   Divide 21 by $\frac{3}{10}$.

$$21 \div \frac{3}{10} =$$

$$\frac{\overset{7}{\cancel{21}}}{1} \times \frac{10}{\underset{1}{\cancel{3}}} = \frac{70}{1} = 70$$

Using a decimal:

STEP 1.   Change 30% to a decimal.

$$30\% = 30\% = .3$$

STEP 2.   Divide 21 by .3.

$$.3)\overline{21.0} \quad 70$$

⇒   There are 70 employees at Carter Supply.

It is a good idea to check these "backwards" problems. To check the example, find 30% of 70. The answer should be 21.

Using a fraction: $30\% = \frac{3}{10}$ Using a decimal: $30\% = .3$

$$\frac{3}{\underset{1}{\cancel{10}}} \times \frac{\overset{7}{\cancel{70}}}{1} = \frac{21}{1} = 21 \qquad\qquad .3 \times 70 = 21.0 = 21$$

Use fractions to solve problems 1 to 10.

1. 80% of what number is 120? $12\frac{1}{2}$% of what number is 15?

2. 50% of what number is 165?   60% of what number is 150?

3. 25% of what number is 19? $16\frac{2}{3}$% of what number is 25?

4. 40% of what number is 34? $37\frac{1}{2}$% of what number is 21?

5. $83\frac{1}{3}$% of what number is 45?   75% of what number is 600?

6. $33\frac{1}{3}$% of what number is 16? $87\frac{1}{2}$% of what number is 140?

7. 80% of the members of a bus drivers' union voted to strike. 216 members voted to strike. How many members are there in the union?

8. Max has saved $265 in order to buy a new amplifier. This is 50% of the price. How much does the amplifier cost?

9. $16\frac{2}{3}$% of the tickets for an all-city basketball tournament were sold the first hour they went on sale. That hour 985 tickets were sold. What was the total number of tickets available for the tournament?

10. Joan spends $540 a month on food for her family. This is 30% of her income. Find her monthly income.

Use decimals to solve problems 11 to 20.

11. 40% of what number is 18?   25% of what number is 312?

12. 90% of what number is 18?   75% of what number is 150?

13. 15% of what number is 48?   20% of what number is 65?

14. 8.5% of what number is 340?   100% of what number is 56?

15. 2.5% of what number is 160?   4.8% of what number is 240?

16. Joe runs a bicycle repair shop. One day he repaired 18 bikes. These were 12% of the total number of bikes in the shop. How many bikes were in the shop?

17. The sales tax in Enrique's state is 6%. He paid $5.34 in sales tax for a new jacket. Find the price of the jacket.

18. Albert got 34 problems right on a math test. His score was 85% correct. How many problems were on the test?

19. Frank paid $287.50 interest on a loan. The interest rate on the loan was 11.5%. What was the total amount of the loan?

20. Robin bought a computer monitor on sale for 20% off. She saved $87. What was the original price of the monitor?

To check your answers, turn to page 120.

Using Proportion to Find the Whole

After the yearly review of employees at Ace Electronics, only 15% of the workers received raises. A total of 42 workers got raises. How many employees are there at Ace?

Again, proportion is a useful way to set up percent problems. Use the model shown here. Remember that you are looking for the whole, the total number of employees at Ace Electronics.

$$\frac{\text{part}}{\text{whole}} = \frac{\%}{100}$$

Example: Use proportion to solve the problem, 15% of what number is 42?

STEP 1. Set up a proportion. 42 is the part, and 15 is the percent. You are looking for the whole. Use w for the whole.

$$\frac{42}{w} = \frac{15}{100}$$

To review proportion shortcuts, turn to page 27.

STEP 2. Find the cross products and solve.

$$w = \frac{\overset{14}{\cancel{42}} \times \overset{20}{\cancel{100}}}{\underset{1}{\cancel{15}}}$$

$$w = 280$$

There are 280 employees at Ace Electronics.

PRACTICE 32

Use proportion to solve each problem.

1. 25% of what number is 13?   60% of what number is 90?

2. 10% of what number is 89?   35% of what number is 63?

3. 17% of what number is 68?   92% of what number is 276?

4. 80% of what number is 220?   3% of what number is 12?

5. 1.5% of what number is 18?   12.5% of what number is 50?

6. 200% of what number is 65?   24% of what number is 96?

7. The Hawks won 52 games last season. They won 65% of the games they played. How many games did the Hawks play?

8. Ten years ago there were 1,430 children in the Westbrook School. That number is 65% of the number today. How many children go to the Westbrook School now?

9. In an election for state representative, Don Adreiotti got 52% of the votes. He got 26,650 votes. How many people voted in the election?

10. In 1970 Americans ate an average of 14.4 pounds of cheese per person. That was 60% of the amount they ate in 1990. Find the average amount of cheese consumed by each American in 1990.

11. Camille works on a commission rate. She gets 5% of the value of the shoes she sells. One day she made $97.15 in commissions. What was the value of the shoes she sold that day?

12. A mining company has found ore that is 20% copper. How many tons of the ore will be needed to get 10 tons of copper?

To check your answers, turn to page 121.

Mixed Percent Problems

You have studied three basic types of percent problems.

Type A, finding a percent of a number. In these problems you have a whole and you want to find a part of it. To find a percent of a number, first change the percent to a fraction or a decimal. Then **multiply** by the fraction or decimal.

Type B, finding what percent one number is of another. In these problems the percent is not given. To find what percent one number is of another, first make a fraction with the part over the whole. Then change the fraction to a percent.

Type C, finding a number when a percent of it is given. In these problems you have the part but not the whole. To find the missing whole, first change the percent to a fraction or a decimal. Then **divide** by the fraction or decimal.

PRACTICE 33

Identify each problem as Type A, B, or C by writing the appropriate letter in the blank. Then solve each problem.

1. _____ 14 is what percent of 28?

2. _____ What is 60% of 125?

3. _____ What percent of 90 is 60?

4. _____ 6 is what percent of 120?

5. _____ Find 80% of 15.

6. _____ 25% of what number is 13?

7. _____ What percent of 360 is 270?

8. _____ What is 95% of 400?

9. _____ 20% of what number is 11?

10. _____ 15 is what percent of 75?

11. _____ What percent of 48 is 16?

12. _____ Find 2.5% of 300.

13. _____ Larry makes $1,960 a month. He spends $490 a month for rent. What percent of his income goes to rent?

14. _____ Petra bought a blouse for $44. The sales tax in her state is 6%. How much was the tax on her blouse?

15. _____ Rachel helped to sell tickets to her community theater production. She sold 75% of all the tickets. Rachel sold 90 tickets. How many tickets were for sale altogether?

16. _____ Fred took a test with 80 questions. He got 75% of the questions right. How many questions did he get right?

17. _____ There are 20 students in Mr. Wiley's math class. 11 of the students are women. The women make up what percent of the class?

18. _____ Last year Dorothy paid $16 a month for phone service. That amount was 80% of what she pays this year. How much does Dorothy pay each month for her phone this year?

19. _____ The Midvale budget for the year is $3,500,000, of which 3% goes for recreation. How much does Midvale spend on recreation in a year?

20. _____ Ann and Tom have paid 60% of their mortgage. So far they have paid $72,000. What was the total amount of their mortgage?

21. _____ Mark started working at a salary of $540 a week. In six months he got a $27 a week raise. The raise was what percent of his old salary?

22. _____ There are 650 employees at Pulp Paper Products. Of these employees, 84% belong to the union. How many employees belong to the union?

23. _____ Sheila earns a 6% commission on all products she sells. Last week, her total sales were $5,300. How much did she earn in commission?

24. _____ Last year, Julissa earned $16,800. She earned $2,688 in February. What percent of her annual income did she earn in the month of February?

To check your answers, turn to page 121.

Finding the Percent and the Whole Review

The problems on pages 93 and 94 will help you decide if you need to review this unit. Solve each problem. When you finish, look at the chart to see which pages you should review.

1. 27 is what percent of 36?

2. What percent of 50 is 45?

3. What percent of 130 is 78?

4. What percent of 40 is 72?

5. Juan works 40 hours a week. He spends 12 hours of his working time driving a company van. His driving time is what percent of his work week?

6. The Michaelsons take home $2,200 a month, and they save $110 a month. What percent of their take-home pay do they save?

7. From 32 to 36 is an increase of what percent?

8. Find the percent of increase from 420 to 588.

9. When Cassie moved into her apartment the rent was $320. Now she pays $480. By what percent did her rent increase?

10. From 75 to 60 is a decrease of what percent?

11. What is the percent of decrease from 720 to 480?

12. A stereo that once sold for $380 was on sale for $323. Find the percent of discount on the original price.

13. 75% of what number is 213?

14. 3.5% of what number is 21?

15. The parents association at the Westbrook School hope to raise enough money to buy new uniforms for the athletic department. So far they have raised $2,700. This is 60% of what they need. How much money are they trying to raise?

PROGRESS CHECK

Check your answers on page 121. Then return to the review pages for the problems you missed. Correct your answers before going on to the next unit.

If you missed problems	*Review pages*
1 to 6	75 to 80
7 to 9	81 to 82
10 to 12	83 to 84
13 to 15	85 to 89

Final Review

These problems will tell you which parts of this book you need to review before going on to *New Basic Skills with Math: Algebra*. When you finish, check the chart to see which pages to review.

Use the following information to answer questions 1 and 2.

> To make a fence for his garden, Steve spent 5 hours cutting wood and 4 hours assembling the pieces.

1. What is the ratio of the time he spent cutting to the time he spent assembling?

2. What is the ratio of the time he spent assembling the fence to the total time he spent?

For problems 3 to 5, simplify each ratio.

3. 28:49

4. 20 to 12

5. 18:360

6. Simplify the ratio of 9 months to 2 years.

7. Simplify the ratio of 4 yards to 8 feet.

For problems 8 to 10, solve each proportion for *m*.

8. $\dfrac{2}{15} = \dfrac{12}{m}$

9. $\dfrac{5}{2} = \dfrac{m}{17}$

10. $6{:}m = 9{:}4$

11. The ratio of green paint to gray paint in a certain mixture is 2:3. Sally used 6 gallons of green paint. How many gallons of gray paint did she use?

12. The scale on a map is 1 inch equals 80 miles. Two towns are 3.25 inches apart on the map. Find the distance between the towns in miles.

13. Ali drove 393 miles on 15 gallons. Find his gas mileage (miles per gallon) to the nearest tenth.

14. For a soup recipe, the ratio of tomato juice to chicken stock is 2:3. Volunteers in a community center made 15 quarts of soup. How many quarts of chicken stock did they need?

Change each decimal to a percent.

15. .02 =

16. .475 =

17. $.09\frac{1}{3} =$

Change each percent to a decimal.

18. 92% =

19. 4% =

20. 0.9% =

Change each fraction to a percent.

21. $\dfrac{12}{25} =$

22. $\dfrac{5}{12} =$

23. $\dfrac{5}{8} =$

Change each percent to a fraction.

24. 36% =

25. 8.5% =

26. $28\frac{4}{7}\% =$

27. Find 40% of 65.

28. Find 35% of 200.

29. Find $16\frac{2}{3}\%$ of 120. **30.** Find $87\frac{1}{2}\%$ of 160.

31. Find 125% of 48. **32.** Find 0.8% of 250.

33. Janet took a test with 40 questions. She got 90% of the questions right. How many questions did she get right?

34. George and Margaret are buying a house for $145,000. They have to make a down payment of 11%. How much is the down payment for the house?

35. Find 8% of $6.29. Round off to the nearest cent.

The circle graph shows the country of origin for motor vehicle production in a recent year. Use the graph to answer questions 36 and 37.

36. What percent of motor vehicles were produced in the U.S.?

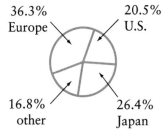

Motor Vehicle Production

36.3% Europe   20.5% U.S.

16.8% other   26.4% Japan

37. For the year shown on the graph, a total of 47,000,000 motor vehicles were produced in the world. How many of them were produced in Japan?

Solve the following.

38. Virginia bought a T.V. on sale. The original price was $245. The T.V. was on sale for 15% off the old price. How much did Virginia pay for the T.V.?

39. In 1985 the town of Eastport spent $3,000,000 on education. In 1995 they spent 40% more than in 1985. How much did they spend on education in 1995?

40. Find the interest on $600 at 9% annual interest for one year.

41. Find the interest on $3,000 at 11% annual interest for eight months.

42. 27 is what % of 72?

43. 18 is what % of 36?

44. 16 is what % of 80?

45. 35 is what % of 42?

46. Jim makes $540 a week. His employer takes out $81 for taxes and social security. What percent of Jim's pay goes to taxes and social security?

47. Ann put $800 in a savings account for a year. She got $48 in interest. The interest was what percent of the amount Ann put in the bank?

48. Usually there are 25 people at the meetings of the Eleventh Street Tenants' Organization. At the last meeting there were only 16 people. What percent of the usual number was absent?

49. Last year Sue paid $450 a month for rent. This year she pays $504 a month. By what percent did her rent go up?

50. 25% of what number is 12?

51. 60% of what number is 90?

52. 87.5% of what number is 35?

53. $83\frac{1}{3}$% of what number is 75?

54. Jeff works on a commission rate. He gets 5% of the value of the clothes he sells. On Saturday he made $125.30 in commissions. What was the value of the clothes he sold that day?

55. Petra got 80% of the problems right on a test. She got 52 problems right. How many problems were on the test?

Check your answers on page 122. Circle the problems you missed on the chart below. Review the pages that show how to work the problems you missed. Then try the problems again.

Problem Number	Review Pages	Problem Number	Review Pages	Problem Number	Review Pages
1	6–10	20	40–41	38	69–71
2	6–10	21	42	39	69–71
3	11–12	22	42	40	66–68
4	11–12	23	42	41	66–68
5	11–12	24	43–45	42	75–80
6	13–17	25	43–45	43	75–80
7	13–17	26	43–45	44	75–80
8	20–28	27	53–57	45	75–80
9	20–28	28	53–57	46	75–80
10	20–28	29	53–57	47	75–80
11	20–28	30	53–57	48	83–84
12	29–30	31	61	49	81–82
13	31–32	32	60	50	85–89
14	33–34	33	53–57	51	85–89
15	39	34	53–57	52	85–89
16	39	35	58–59	53	85–89
17	39	36	63–65	54	85–89
18	40–41	37	63–65	55	85–89
19	40–41				

Answers

Ratios and Percents Preview
pages 1–5

1. 5:6
2. 5:11
3. 2:3
4. 7 to 5
5. 1:10
6. 1:4
7. 7:12
8. $3\frac{3}{5}$
9. $22\frac{1}{2}$
10. $\frac{2}{3}$
11. 230 miles
12. 84 miles
13. $4.45
14. 8 women
15. 40%
16. 4%
17. 22.5%
18. .09
19. $.03\frac{1}{3}$
20. 2.5
21. 65%
22. $43\frac{3}{4}\%$
23. 18%
24. $\frac{4}{25}$
25. $\frac{9}{200}$
26. $\frac{4}{9}$
27. 21
28. 31
29. 24
30. 250
31. 27
32. 3.6
33. $8,400
34. 253,000 people
35. $.45
36. 9.7%
37. $37,000
38. $21.06
39. $348.60
40. $48
41. $65
42. 40%
43. $66\frac{2}{3}\%$
44. 90%
45. 32%
46. 10%
47. 60%
48. 75%
49. 15%
50. 135
51. 96
52. 120
53. 140
54. 168 members
55. $1,800

What Is a Ratio?
Practice 1
pages 7–8

1. 5 to 2
2. $\frac{5}{2}$
3. 5
4. 2
5. 2
6. $\frac{2}{5}$
7. 2 to 5
8. 4
9. 3
10. 7
11. 3:4
12. 4:3
13. 4:7
14. 3:7
15. four   three

Writing Ratios from Words
Practice 2
pages 9–10

A.

1. $\frac{83}{2}$

2. $\frac{1}{25}$

3. $\frac{3}{\$1.99}$

4. $\frac{5}{2}$

5. $\frac{\$25}{3}$

6. $\frac{2}{3}$

7. 4:9

8. \$28:3

9. 800:5

10. 100:7

11. 1:5

12. 2:135

B.

13. $\frac{55}{1}$

14. $\frac{26}{1}$

15. $\frac{24}{1}$

16. $\frac{\$9}{1}$

17. $\frac{4}{1}$

18. $\frac{3}{1}$

19. 50 to 1

20. \$9,500 to 1

21. 144 to 1

22. \$25 to 1

23. 2 to 1

24. 10 to 1

25. 13:6

26. 6 to 13

27. 13 + 6 = 19 employees

28. $\frac{13}{19}$

29. $\frac{6}{19}$

Simplifying Ratios
Practice 3
pages 11–13

1. 15:25 = 3:5

2. 36:45 = 4:5

3. 21:56 = 3:8

4. 32:40 = 4:5

5. 13 to 26 = 1 to 2

6. 18 to 2 = 9 to 1

7. 4 to 48 = 1 to 12

8. 27 to 30 = 9 to 10

9. $\frac{12}{60} = \frac{1}{5}$

10. $\frac{22}{20} = \frac{11}{10}$

11. $\frac{5}{1,000} = \frac{1}{200}$

12. $\frac{250}{25} = \frac{10}{1}$

13. 52:2 = 26:1

14. 45:3 = 15:1

15. 2:30 = 1:15

16. 4:10 = 2:5

17. 200:8 = 25:1

18. 300:10 = 30:1

19. $\frac{\$1,600}{\$800} = \frac{2}{1}$

20. $\frac{\$800}{\$1,600} = \frac{1}{2}$

21. $\frac{\$1,600}{\$2,400} = \frac{2}{3}$

22. $\frac{\$800}{\$2,400} = \frac{1}{3}$

23. total = 6 + 2 = 8 $\frac{6}{8} = \frac{3}{4}$

24. $\frac{2}{8} = \frac{1}{4}$

Ratio of Measurements
Practice 4
pages 14–17

1. 20:60 = 1:3

2. 8:12 = 2:3

3. 8:24 = 1:3

4. 10:60 = 1:6

5. 6:14 = 3:7

6. 30:12 = 5:2

7. $30:24 = 5:4$

8. $2:28 = 1:14$

9. $1:36$

10. $24:100 = 6:25$

11. 2 hr 30 min = 150 min $30:150 = 1:5$

12. 4 hr = 240 min $48:240 = 1:5$

13. 1 hr 40 min = 100 min $12:100 = 3:25$

14. $\frac{8}{12} = \frac{2}{3}$

15. $\frac{1}{3}$

16. $\frac{5,280}{2,640} = \frac{2}{1}$

17. $\frac{24}{16} = \frac{3}{2}$

18. $\frac{9}{15} = \frac{3}{5}$

19. $\frac{9}{48} = \frac{3}{16}$

20. $\frac{30}{36} = \frac{5}{6}$

21. $\frac{5,280}{528} = \frac{10}{1}$

22. $\frac{60}{100} = \frac{3}{5}$

23. $\frac{8}{6} = \frac{4}{3}$

24. 3 ft = 36 in. $\frac{3 \text{ in.}}{36 \text{ in.}} = \frac{1}{12}$

25. 10 ft = 120 in. $\frac{8 \text{ in.}}{120 \text{ in.}} = \frac{1}{15}$

26. 1 to 4

27. 20 to 16 = 5 to 4

28. 8 to 3

29. 8 to 10 = 4 to 5

30. 10 to 1

31. 1 quart = 2 pints = 4 cups   4 to 3

32. 1 gal = 4 quarts = 8 pints = 16 cups $16 \times 5 = 80$ cups   1 to 80

33. $\frac{12}{16} = \frac{3}{4}$

34. $\frac{500}{2,000} = \frac{1}{4}$

35. $\frac{20}{32} = \frac{5}{8}$

36. $\frac{5,000}{4,000} = \frac{5}{4}$

37. $\frac{4}{48} = \frac{1}{12}$

38. $\frac{2,000}{100} = \frac{20}{1}$

39. $\frac{30}{16} = \frac{15}{8}$

40. $\frac{1,500}{6,000} = \frac{1}{4}$

41. 2 pounds = 32 ounces

$\frac{4}{32} = \frac{1}{8}$

42. $\frac{1,400}{1,600} = \frac{7}{8}$

Ratio Review
pages 18–19

1. 3   10

2. 10:3 or 10 to 3 or $\frac{10}{3}$

3. 99:1 or 99 to 1 or $\frac{99}{1}$

4. 1:100 or 1 to 100 or $\frac{1}{100}$

5. 3:4

6. 42:1

7. 5 to 2

8. 9:2

9. $10:12 = 5:6$

10. $40:120 = 1:3$

1. 40
2. 40
3. Yes
4. Yes
5. 12
6. 13
7. No
8. No

9. $4 \times 10 = 5 \times 8$
$40 = 40$

$7 \times 12 = 4 \times 21$
$84 = 84$

$15 \times 4 = 10 \times 6$
$60 = 60$

10. $6 \times 3 = 1 \times 18$
$18 = 18$

$2 \times 28 = 7 \times 8$
$56 = 56$

$24 \times 1 = 6 \times 4$
$24 = 24$

11. $2 \times 20 = 5 \times 8$
$40 = 40$

$108 \times 1 = 9 \times 12$
$108 = 108$

$7 \times 27 = 9 \times 21$
$189 = 189$

12. $\frac{5}{25} = \frac{10}{50}$
$5 \times 50 = 25 \times 10$
$250 = 250$

$\frac{16}{6} = \frac{8}{3}$
$16 \times 3 = 6 \times 8$
$48 = 48$

$\frac{4}{1} = \frac{36}{9}$
$4 \times 9 = 1 \times 36$
$36 = 36$

13. $\frac{30}{70} = \frac{3}{7}$
$30 \times 7 = 70 \times 3$
$210 = 210$

$\frac{1}{8} = \frac{6}{48}$
$1 \times 48 = 8 \times 6$
$48 = 48$

$\frac{12}{9} = \frac{16}{12}$
$12 \times 12 = 9 \times 16$
$144 = 144$

14. total : right = 5:4
15. total : right = 20:16
16. Yes, because the cross products are equal. $\frac{5}{4} = \frac{20}{16}$

$$5 \times 16 = 4 \times 20$$
$$80 = 80$$

A.

1. $\frac{5}{6} = \frac{15}{a}$
$5 \times a = 90$
$a = 90 \div 5$
$a = \mathbf{18}$

$\frac{10}{8} = \frac{a}{16}$
$160 = 8 \times a$
$160 \div 8 = a$
$20 = a$

$\frac{4}{a} = \frac{12}{18}$
$72 = 12 \times a$
$72 \div 12 = a$
$6 = a$

2. $\frac{a}{40} = \frac{6}{20}$
$20 \times a = 240$
$a = 240 \div 20$
$a = \mathbf{12}$

$\frac{5}{3} = \frac{25}{a}$
$5 \times a = 75$
$a = 75 \div 5$
$a = \mathbf{15}$

$\frac{18}{21} = \frac{a}{7}$
$126 = 21 \times a$
$126 \div 21 = a$
$6 = a$

3.
$$\frac{2}{a} = \frac{8}{12}$$
$$24 = 8 \times a$$
$$24 \div 8 = a$$
$$3 = a$$

$$\frac{14}{7} = \frac{12}{a}$$
$$14 \times a = 84$$
$$a = 84 \div 14$$
$$a = 6$$

$$\frac{a}{10} = \frac{27}{30}$$
$$30 \times a = 270$$
$$a = 270 \div 30$$
$$a = 9$$

4.
$$7{:}4 = 28{:}x$$
$$\frac{7}{4} = \frac{28}{x}$$
$$7 \times x = 112$$
$$x = 112 \div 7$$
$$x = 16$$

$$2{:}9 = x{:}45$$
$$\frac{2}{9} = \frac{x}{45}$$
$$90 = 9 \times x$$
$$90 \div 9 = x$$
$$10 = x$$

$$6{:}x = 30{:}40$$
$$\frac{6}{x} = \frac{30}{40}$$
$$240 = 30 \times x$$
$$240 \div 30 = x$$
$$8 = x$$

5.
$$x{:}24 = 7{:}3$$
$$\frac{x}{24} = \frac{7}{3}$$
$$3 \times x = 168$$
$$x = 168 \div 3$$
$$x = 56$$

$$22{:}16 = 11{:}x$$
$$\frac{22}{16} = \frac{11}{x}$$
$$22 \times x = 176$$
$$x = 176 \div 22$$
$$x = 8$$

$$45{:}60 = x{:}4$$
$$\frac{45}{60} = \frac{x}{4}$$
$$180 = 60 \times x$$
$$180 \div 60 = x$$
$$3 = x$$

6.
$$5{:}x = 10{:}8$$
$$\frac{5}{x} = \frac{10}{8}$$
$$40 = 10 \times x$$
$$40 \div 10 = x$$
$$4 = x$$

$$x{:}15 = 2{:}1$$
$$\frac{x}{15} = \frac{2}{1}$$
$$1 \times x = 30$$
$$x = 30 \div 1$$
$$x = 30$$

$$7{:}10 = 21{:}x$$
$$\frac{7}{10} = \frac{21}{x}$$
$$7 \times x = 210$$
$$x = 210 \div 7$$
$$x = 30$$

B.

7.
$$\frac{2}{3} = \frac{5}{e}$$
$$2 \times e = 15$$
$$e = 15 \div 2$$
$$e = 7\frac{1}{2}$$

$$\frac{7}{4} = \frac{e}{9}$$
$$63 = 4 \times e$$
$$63 \div 4 = e$$
$$15\frac{3}{4} = e$$

$$\frac{10}{e} = \frac{3}{8}$$
$$80 = 3 \times e$$
$$80 \div 3 = e$$
$$26\frac{2}{3} = e$$

8.
$$\frac{e}{15} = \frac{3}{4}$$
$$4 \times e = 45$$
$$e = 45 \div 4$$
$$e = 11\frac{1}{4}$$

$$\frac{9}{20} = \frac{4}{e}$$
$$9 \times e = 80$$
$$e = 80 \div 9$$
$$e = 8\frac{8}{9}$$

$$\frac{3}{2} = \frac{e}{5}$$
$$15 = 2 \times e$$
$$15 \div 2 = e$$
$$7\frac{1}{2} = e$$

9.
$$\frac{7}{10} = \frac{e}{5}$$
$$7 \times 5 = 10 \times e$$
$$35 = 10 \times e$$
$$35 \div 10 = e$$
$$3.5 \text{ or } 3\frac{1}{2} = e$$

$$\frac{e}{25} = \frac{5}{6}$$
$$e \times 6 = 25 \times 5$$
$$e \times 6 = 125$$
$$e = 125 \div 6$$
$$e = 20\frac{5}{6}$$

$$\frac{5}{8} = \frac{12}{e}$$
$$5 \times e = 8 \times 12$$
$$5 \times e = 96$$
$$e = 96 \div 5$$
$$e = 19\frac{1}{5}$$

10.

$6:11 = 2:d$

$\frac{6}{11} = \frac{2}{d}$

$6 \times d = 22$

$d = 22 \div 6$

$d = 3\frac{2}{3}$

$3:5 = d:8$

$\frac{3}{5} = \frac{d}{8}$

$24 = 5 \times d$

$24 \div 5 = d$

$4\frac{4}{5} = d$

$16:d = 3:2$

$\frac{16}{d} = \frac{3}{2}$

$32 = 3 \times d$

$32 \div 3 = d$

$10\frac{2}{3} = d$

11.

$d:9 = 4:5$

$\frac{d}{9} = \frac{4}{5}$

$5 \times d = 36$

$d = 36 \div 5$

$d = 7\frac{1}{5}$

$20:3 = 9:d$

$\frac{20}{3} = \frac{9}{d}$

$20 \times d = 27$

$d = 27 \div 20$

$d = 1\frac{7}{20}$

$2:15 = d:4$

$\frac{2}{15} = \frac{d}{4}$

$8 = 15 \times d$

$8 \div 15 = d$

$\frac{8}{15} = d$

C.

12. $\dfrac{\text{won}}{\text{lost}} \; \dfrac{4}{3} = \dfrac{12}{n}$

$4 \times n = 36$

$n = 36 \div 4$

$n = 9 \text{ games}$

13. $\dfrac{\text{acres}}{\text{bushels}} \; \dfrac{8}{280} = \dfrac{20}{n}$

$8 \times n = 5{,}600$

$n = 5{,}600 \div 8$

$n = 700 \text{ bushels}$

14. $\dfrac{\text{width}}{\text{length}} \; \dfrac{4}{5} = \dfrac{x}{20}$

$5 \times x = 80$

$x = 80 \div 5$

$x = 16 \text{ inches}$

15. $\dfrac{\text{flour}}{\text{butter}} \; \dfrac{6}{4} = \dfrac{4}{x}$

$6 \times x = 16$

$x = 16 \div 6$

$x = 2\frac{2}{3} \text{ tablespoons}$

16. $\dfrac{\text{hits}}{\text{games}} \; \dfrac{8}{5} = \dfrac{x}{30}$

$5 \times x = 240$

$x = 240 \div 5$

$x = 48 \text{ hits}$

17. $\dfrac{\text{miles}}{\text{hours}} \; \dfrac{144}{3} = \dfrac{x}{5}$

$3 \times x = 720$

$x = 720 \div 3$

$x = 240 \text{ miles}$

18. $\dfrac{\text{pounds}}{\text{people}} \; \dfrac{5}{6} = \dfrac{x}{9}$

$6 \times x = 45$

$x = 45 \div 6$

$x = 7\frac{1}{2} \text{ pounds}$

19. $\dfrac{\text{cost}}{\text{pounds}} \; \dfrac{\$7.78}{2} = \dfrac{x}{3}$

$2 \times x = \$23.34$

$x = \$23.34 \div 2$

$x = \$11.67$

20. $\dfrac{\text{wage}}{\text{food}} \; \dfrac{\$10}{\$3} = \dfrac{\$490}{x}$

$10 \times x = \$1470$

$x = \$1470 \div 10$

$x = \$147$

21. $\dfrac{\text{won}}{\text{played}} \; \dfrac{3}{4} = \dfrac{12}{x}$

$3 \times x = 48$

$x = 48 \div 3$

$x = 16 \text{ games}$

Proportion Shortcuts
Practice 7
pages 27–28

1. $\dfrac{20}{50} = \dfrac{m}{45}$

$$m = \dfrac{\overset{2}{\cancel{20}} \times \overset{9}{\cancel{45}}}{\underset{\underset{1}{\cancel{8}}}{\cancel{50}}}$$

$m = 18$

$\dfrac{32}{200} = \dfrac{48}{m}$

$$m = \dfrac{\overset{100}{\cancel{200}} \times \overset{3}{\cancel{48}}}{\underset{\underset{1}{\cancel{2}}}{\cancel{32}}}$$

$m = 300$

$\dfrac{500}{m} = \dfrac{300}{12}$

$$m = \dfrac{\overset{5}{\cancel{500}} \times \overset{4}{\cancel{12}}}{\underset{\underset{1}{\cancel{3}}}{\cancel{300}}}$$

$m = 20$

2. $\dfrac{15}{60} = \dfrac{45}{m}$

$$m = \dfrac{60 \times \overset{3}{\cancel{45}}}{\underset{1}{\cancel{15}}}$$

$m = 180$

$\dfrac{m}{120} = \dfrac{18}{144}$

$$m = \dfrac{\overset{\overset{5}{\cancel{10}}}{\cancel{120}} \times \overset{3}{\cancel{18}}}{\underset{\underset{\underset{1}{\cancel{2}}}{\cancel{12}}}{\cancel{144}}}$$

$m = 15$

$\dfrac{20}{350} = \dfrac{16}{m}$

$$m = \dfrac{\overset{70}{\cancel{350}} \times \overset{4}{\cancel{16}}}{\underset{\underset{1}{\cancel{5}}}{\cancel{20}}}$$

$m = 280$

3. $\dfrac{n}{340} = \dfrac{6}{17}$

$$n = \dfrac{\overset{20}{\cancel{340}} \times 6}{\underset{1}{\cancel{17}}}$$

$n = 120$

$\dfrac{6}{25} = \dfrac{n}{750}$

$$n = \dfrac{6 \times \overset{30}{\cancel{750}}}{\underset{1}{\cancel{25}}}$$

$n = 180$

$\dfrac{30}{80} = \dfrac{24}{n}$

$$n = \dfrac{\overset{8}{\cancel{80}} \times \overset{8}{\cancel{24}}}{\underset{\underset{1}{\cancel{3}}}{\cancel{30}}}$$

$n = 64$

4. $\dfrac{300}{n} = \dfrac{60}{9}$

$$n = \dfrac{\overset{5}{\cancel{300}} \times 9}{\underset{1}{\cancel{60}}}$$

$n = 45$

$\dfrac{250}{19} = \dfrac{1{,}000}{n}$

$$n = \dfrac{19 \times \overset{4}{\cancel{1000}}}{\underset{1}{\cancel{250}}}$$

$n = 76$

$\dfrac{400}{15} = \dfrac{n}{90}$

$$n = \dfrac{400 \times \overset{6}{\cancel{90}}}{\underset{1}{\cancel{15}}}$$

$n = 2{,}400$

5. $\dfrac{\text{miles}}{\text{hours}} \ \dfrac{1{,}440}{3} = \dfrac{d}{5}$

$$d = \dfrac{\overset{480}{1{,}440} \times 5}{\underset{1}{\cancel{3}}}$$

$d = 2{,}400$ miles

6. $\dfrac{\text{price}}{\text{gallons}} \ \dfrac{\$30.50}{2} = \dfrac{n}{10}$

$$n = \dfrac{\$30.50 \times \overset{5}{\cancel{10}}}{\underset{1}{\cancel{2}}}$$

$n = \$152.50$

7. $\dfrac{\text{divorces}}{\text{people}} \ \dfrac{5}{1000} = \dfrac{n}{13{,}000}$

$$n = \dfrac{5 \times \overset{13}{\cancel{13{,}000}}}{\underset{1}{\cancel{1000}}}$$

$n = 65$ divorces

8. $\dfrac{\text{coupons}}{\text{full price}} \ \dfrac{2}{5} = \dfrac{w}{130}$

$$w = \dfrac{2 \times \overset{26}{\cancel{130}}}{\underset{1}{\cancel{5}}}$$

$w = 52$ customers using coupons

9. $\dfrac{\text{raises}}{\text{total}}\ \dfrac{3}{20} = \dfrac{n}{1,200}$

$$n = \dfrac{3 \times \overset{60}{\cancel{1,200}}}{\underset{1}{\cancel{20}}}$$

$$n = 180 \text{ workers}$$

10. $\dfrac{\text{acres}}{\text{bushels}}\ \dfrac{6}{720} = \dfrac{48}{n}$

$$n = \dfrac{720 \times \overset{8}{\cancel{48}}}{\underset{1}{\cancel{6}}}$$

$$n = 5,760 \text{ bushels}$$

Map Scales
Practice 8
page 30

1. $\dfrac{\text{inches}}{\text{miles}}\ \dfrac{1}{80} = \dfrac{1}{d}$

$$d = \dfrac{80 \times 1}{1}$$

$$d = 80 \text{ miles}$$

2. $\dfrac{\text{inches}}{\text{miles}}\ \dfrac{1}{80} = \dfrac{1.5}{d}$

$$d = \dfrac{80 \times 1.5}{1}$$

$$d = 120 \text{ miles}$$

3. $\dfrac{\text{inches}}{\text{miles}}\ \dfrac{1}{200} = \dfrac{3.5}{d}$

$$d = \dfrac{200 \times 3.5}{1}$$

$$d = 700 \text{ miles}$$

4. $\dfrac{\text{centimeters}}{\text{kilometers}}\ \dfrac{1}{20} = \dfrac{1.75}{d}$

$$d = \dfrac{20 \times 1.75}{1}$$

$$d = 35 \text{ km}$$

5. $\dfrac{\text{inches}}{\text{miles}}\ \dfrac{1}{25} = \dfrac{d}{300}$

$$d = \dfrac{300 \times 1}{25}$$

$$d = 12 \text{ inches}$$

6. $\dfrac{\text{inches}}{\text{miles}}\ \dfrac{1}{60} = \dfrac{20}{d}$

$$d = \dfrac{60 \times 20}{1}$$

$$d = 1,200 \text{ miles}$$

7. $\dfrac{\text{inches}}{\text{feet}}\ \dfrac{1}{2,000} = \dfrac{2.5}{d}$

$$d = \dfrac{2,000 \times 2.5}{1}$$

$$d = 5,000 \text{ feet}$$

8. $\dfrac{\text{inches}}{\text{miles}}\ \dfrac{1}{40} = \dfrac{12.5}{d}$

$$d = \dfrac{40 \times 12.5}{1}$$

$$d = 500 \text{ miles}$$

Finding Unit Rates
Practice 9
pages 31–32

1. $\dfrac{\text{miles}}{\text{gallons}}\ \dfrac{252}{18} = \dfrac{m}{1}$

$$m = \dfrac{252 \times 1}{18}$$

$$m = 14 \text{ mpg}$$

2. $\dfrac{\text{points}}{\text{games}}\ \dfrac{2,383}{80} = \dfrac{x}{1}$

$$x = \dfrac{2,383 \times 1}{80}$$

$$x = 29.7 \text{ to the nearest}$$
$$\text{whole} = 30 \text{ points}$$

3. $\dfrac{\text{yards}}{\text{completions}}\ \dfrac{357}{23} = \dfrac{x}{1}$

$$x = \dfrac{357 \times 1}{23}$$

$$x = 15.5 \text{ to the}$$
$$\text{nearest whole}$$
$$= 16 \text{ yards}$$

4. $\dfrac{\text{cost}}{\text{ticket}}\ \dfrac{\$38.25}{3} = \dfrac{x}{1}$

$$x = \dfrac{\$38.25 \times 1}{3}$$

$$x = \$12.75$$

5. $\dfrac{\text{people}}{\text{years}} \dfrac{4000}{10} = \dfrac{x}{1}$

$$x = \dfrac{4000 \times 1}{10}$$
$$x = \textbf{400 people}$$

6. $\dfrac{\text{cost}}{\text{people}} \dfrac{\$357.50}{13} = \dfrac{x}{1}$

$$x = \dfrac{\$357.50 \times 1}{13}$$
$$x = \textbf{\$27.50}$$

7. $\$26{,}500 + \$8{,}200 = \$34{,}700$

$\dfrac{\text{income}}{\text{people}} \dfrac{\$34{,}700}{5} = \dfrac{x}{1}$

$$x = \dfrac{\$34{,}700 \times 1}{5}$$
$$x = \textbf{\$6{,}940}$$

8. $\dfrac{\text{cost}}{\text{ounces}} \dfrac{\$3.99}{20} = \dfrac{x}{1}$

$$x = \dfrac{\$3.99 \times 1}{20}$$
$$x = \$.199 \text{ to the}$$
$$\text{nearest cent} = \textbf{\$.20}$$

9. $\dfrac{\text{cost}}{\text{ounces}} \dfrac{\$2.69}{15} = \dfrac{x}{1}$

$$x = \dfrac{\$2.69 \times 1}{15}$$
$$x = \$.179 \text{ to the}$$
$$\text{nearest cent} = \textbf{\$.18}$$

10. $\dfrac{\text{cost}}{\text{ounces}} \dfrac{\$1.47}{6} = \dfrac{x}{\dfrac{\$1.47 \times 1}{6}}$

$$x =$$
$$x = \$.245 \text{ to the}$$
$$\text{nearest cent} = \textbf{\$.25}$$

11. Brand Y is the best buy.

Multi-Step Proportions
Practice 10
pages 33–34

1. $3 + 1 = 4$ played

$\dfrac{\text{won}}{\text{played}} \dfrac{3}{4} = \dfrac{x}{36}$

$$x = \dfrac{3 \times 36}{4}$$
$$x = \textbf{27 games won}$$

2. $1 + 4 = 5$ total

$\dfrac{\text{white}}{\text{total}} \dfrac{1}{5} = \dfrac{x}{15}$

$$x = \dfrac{1 \times 15}{5}$$
$$x = \textbf{3 gallons white}$$

3. $2 + 3 = 5$ total

$\dfrac{\text{in shop}}{\text{total}} \dfrac{2}{5} = \dfrac{x}{20}$

$$x = \dfrac{2 \times 20}{5}$$
$$x = \textbf{8 days in shop}$$

4. $5 - 4 = 1$ wrong

$\dfrac{\text{wrong}}{\text{total}} \dfrac{1}{5} = \dfrac{x}{25}$

$$x = \dfrac{1 \times 25}{5}$$
$$x = \textbf{5 problems wrong}$$

5. $3 + 7 = 10$ take home

$\dfrac{\text{rent}}{\text{take home}} \dfrac{3}{10} = \dfrac{x}{400}$

$$x = \dfrac{3 \times 400}{10}$$
$$x = \textbf{\$120 for rent}$$

6. $\dfrac{\text{students with work experience}}{\text{total students}} \dfrac{1}{9} = \dfrac{x}{27}$

$$x = \dfrac{27 \times 1}{9}$$
$$x = \textbf{3 students have}$$
$$\textbf{work experience}$$

7.
$$1 + 5 = 6 \text{ total}$$
$$\frac{\text{smokers}}{\text{total workers}} \quad \frac{1}{6} = \frac{3}{x}$$
$$x = \frac{6 \times 3}{1}$$
$$x = \mathbf{18 \text{ total}}$$

8.
$$2 + 19 = 21 \text{ total}$$
$$\frac{\text{walk}}{\text{total}} \quad \frac{2}{21} = \frac{x}{252}$$
$$x = \frac{2 \times 252}{21}$$
$$x = \mathbf{24 \text{ walkers}}$$

9.
$$\frac{\text{adults}}{\text{children}} \quad \frac{1}{5} = \frac{x}{60}$$
$$x = \frac{1 \times 60}{5}$$
$$x = \mathbf{12 \text{ adults}}$$
$$12 \text{ adults} + 60 \text{ children} = \mathbf{72 \text{ total}}$$

Proportion Review
pages 35–36

1.
$$\frac{3}{8} = \frac{12}{n}$$
$$n = \frac{8 \times 12}{3}$$
$$n = \mathbf{32}$$

2.
$$\frac{25}{6} = \frac{n}{4}$$
$$n = \frac{25 \times 4}{6}$$
$$n = \mathbf{16\frac{2}{3}}$$

3. $3:20 = n:150$
$$\frac{3}{20} = \frac{n}{150}$$
$$n = \frac{3 \times 150}{20}$$
$$n = \mathbf{22\frac{1}{2}}$$

4.
$$\frac{5}{n} = \frac{2}{3}$$
$$n = \frac{5 \times 3}{2}$$
$$n = \mathbf{7\frac{1}{2}}$$

5.
$$\frac{n}{15} = \frac{1}{6}$$
$$n = \frac{15 \times 1}{6}$$
$$n = \mathbf{2\frac{1}{2}}$$

6. $n:9 = 7:30$
$$\frac{n}{9} = \frac{7}{30}$$
$$n = \frac{9 \times 7}{30}$$
$$n = \mathbf{2\frac{1}{10}}$$

7.
$$\frac{\text{miles}}{\text{hours}} \quad \frac{105}{2} = \frac{d}{7}$$
$$d = \frac{105 \times 7}{2}$$
$$d = \mathbf{367\frac{1}{2} \text{ miles}}$$

8.
$$\frac{\text{wins}}{\text{loses}} \quad \frac{3}{2} = \frac{9}{x}$$
$$x = \frac{2 \times 9}{3}$$
$$x = \mathbf{6 \text{ games}}$$

9.
$$\frac{\text{inches}}{\text{miles}} \quad \frac{1}{60} = \frac{2.5}{x}$$
$$x = \frac{60 \times 2.5}{1}$$
$$x = \mathbf{150 \text{ miles}}$$

10.
$$\frac{\text{inches}}{\text{miles}} \quad \frac{1}{20} = \frac{6.25}{x}$$
$$x = \frac{6.25 \times 20}{1}$$
$$x = \mathbf{125 \text{ miles}}$$

11. $\dfrac{\text{cost}}{\text{pounds}}\ \dfrac{\$13.09}{2.2}=\dfrac{x}{1}$

$$x=\dfrac{\$13.09\times 1}{2.2}$$

$$x=\$5.95$$

12. $\dfrac{\text{miles}}{\text{gallons}}\ \dfrac{319}{11}=\dfrac{x}{1}$

$$x=\dfrac{319\times 1}{11}$$

$$x=\textbf{29 mpg}$$

13. $\dfrac{\text{bushels}}{\text{acres}}\ \dfrac{1{,}122}{33}=\dfrac{x}{1}$

$$x=\dfrac{1{,}122\times 1}{33}$$

$$x=\textbf{34 bu. per acre}$$

14. $5+1=6$ total

$\dfrac{\text{right}}{\text{total}}\ \dfrac{5}{6}=\dfrac{x}{90}$

$$x=\dfrac{5\times 90}{6}$$

$$x=\textbf{75 right}$$

15. $3+5=8$ total

$\dfrac{\text{women}}{\text{total}}\ \dfrac{5}{8}=\dfrac{x}{24}$

$$x=\dfrac{5\times 24}{8}$$

$$x=\textbf{15 women}$$

16. $3+2=5$ total

$\dfrac{\text{typing}}{\text{total}}\ \dfrac{3}{5}=\dfrac{x}{40}$

$$x=\dfrac{3\times 40}{5}$$

$$x=\textbf{24 hours typing}$$

What Is a Percent?
Practice 11
page 38

A.

1. $100\%-40\%=60\%$
2. $100\%-80\%=20\%$
3. $100\%-1\%=99\%$
4. $100\%-66\%=34\%$

B.

5. $4\times 100\%=400\%$
6. $10\times 100\%=1000\%$

Changing Decimals to Percents
Practice 12
page 40

1. 45%	8%	1.5%	$66\frac{2}{3}\%$
2. 60%	15%	$8\frac{1}{3}\%$	96%
3. .8%	40%	1%	50%
4. 160%	24%	37.5%	90%
5. 225%	500%	2%	$6\frac{2}{3}\%$

Changing Percents to Decimals
Practice 13
page 41

1. .15   .06   .625

2. .01   .087 $.16\frac{2}{3}$

3. .4   1.25   .6

4. .003   .05   10

5. $.12\frac{1}{2}$ 2 $.01\frac{1}{4}$

6. .063   .17   .484

7. .65   .045   .002

Changing Fractions to Percents
Practice 14
page 42

1. 90%   80% $22\frac{2}{9}$%   6%

2. 16% $12\frac{1}{2}$% or 12.5% $66\frac{2}{3}$%   50%

3. $83\frac{1}{3}$% $57\frac{1}{7}$%   7% $37\frac{1}{2}$% or 37.5%

Changing Percents to Fractions
Practice 15
pages 43–46

A.

1. $\frac{3}{20}$ $\frac{1}{100}$ $\frac{12}{25}$ $\frac{9}{10}$

2. $\frac{11}{50}$ $\frac{2}{25}$ $1\frac{1}{4}$ $\frac{1}{25}$

3. $\frac{11}{25}$ $\frac{17}{20}$ $\frac{49}{50}$ $2\frac{9}{20}$

4. $\frac{3}{25}$ 5. $\frac{9}{10}$ 6. $\frac{1}{5}$

B.

7. $\frac{7}{250}$ $\frac{5}{8}$ $\frac{3}{200}$ $\frac{51}{500}$

8. $\frac{1}{2000}$ $\frac{23}{200}$ $\frac{7}{8}$ $\frac{1}{80}$

9. $\frac{1}{8}$ 10. $\frac{17}{200}$ 11. $\frac{41}{250}$ 12. $\frac{3}{80}$

13. $\frac{1}{6}$ $\frac{3}{8}$ $\frac{1}{12}$ $\frac{1}{16}$

14. $\frac{8}{9}$ $\frac{5}{6}$ $\frac{4}{7}$ $\frac{1}{24}$

15. $\frac{2}{3}$ 16. $\frac{7}{80}$ 17. $\frac{4}{15}$

Common Fractions, Decimals, and Percents
Practice 16
page 46

1. $.5, \frac{1}{2}$ $.25, \frac{1}{4}$ $.75, \frac{3}{4}$ $.12\frac{1}{2}$ or $.125, \frac{1}{8}$

2. $.37\frac{1}{2}$ or $.375, \frac{3}{8}$ $.62\frac{1}{2}$ or $.625, \frac{5}{8}$ $.87\frac{1}{2}$ or $.875, \frac{7}{8}$ $.33\frac{1}{3}, \frac{1}{3}$

3. $.66\frac{2}{3}, \frac{2}{3}$ $.2, \frac{1}{5}$ $.4, \frac{2}{5}$ $.6, \frac{3}{5}$

4. $.8, \frac{4}{5}$ $.1, \frac{1}{10}$ $.3, \frac{3}{10}$ $.7, \frac{7}{10}$

5. $.9, \frac{9}{10}$ $.16\frac{2}{3}, \frac{1}{6}$ $.83\frac{1}{3}, \frac{5}{6}$

Identifying the Percent, the Whole, and the Part
Practice 17
pages 48–50

A.

	%	whole	part
1.	25%	36	9
2.	75%	20	15
3.	$33\frac{1}{3}$%	36	12
4.	90%	200	180
5.	80%	40	32
6.	50%	$400	$200

B.

7. the part   8. the percent   9. the part

10. the whole   11. the percent   12. the whole

13. the part   14. the percent   15. the part

16. the percent   17. the part   18. the percent

19. the part   20. the whole   21. the percent

Understanding Percent Review
pages 51–52

1. $100\% - 85\% = 15\%$ 2. $100\% - 60\% = 40\%$

3. $3 \times 100\% = 300\%$ 4. 25%

5. 7.9%   6. $3\frac{1}{3}$%

7. .2   8. .0625

9. 1.75   10. 35%

11. $88\frac{8}{9}$%   12. $83\frac{1}{3}$%

13. $\frac{4}{25}$ 14. $\frac{9}{200}$

15. $\frac{2}{75}$ 16. 34

17. 48   18. the part

Finding the Part
Practice 18
pages 54–55

A.

1. 21	28	9.6
2. 12	48	57
3. 12	6	72
4. 18	23	14
5. 8	59.5	12
6. 40.8	53.4	161.6
7. $9,975	*8.* $3.90	
9. 94,250	*10.* $15,900	

B.

11. 32	30	36
12. 45	48	24
13. 91	54	12
14. 306	200	60
15. 48	25	189

16. 48 problems
17. $1,500
18. $1,500

Using Proportion to Find the Part
Practice 19
pages 56–57

1. 12	69	51
2. 21	51	56
3. 161	99	2,850
4. 323.2	13.5	32
5. 47	240	49.5
6. $4,200	*7.* 825 people	
8. $10	*9.* 15 games	
10. 28 women	*11.* $81	
12. 187 beds		

Rounding Money
Practice 20
page 59

1. $.33	$.20	$.82
2. $.74	$1.19	$3.82
3. $.24	$.09	$5.14
4. $.32	$3.32	$.95
5. $.91	$.33	$3.66

6. $3.05   7. $1.74
8. $10.85   9. $.89
10. $94.80

Less than 1%
Practice 21
page 60
1. 1.24   .56   2.4
2. 2.25   6   18.9
3. $3 $.40 $5.04
4. $1,325   5. 88,000 people

More than 100%
Practice 22
page 61
1. 75   920   77
2. 72   1,120   221
3. $100 $160 $4.08
4. 17,920   5. 154 men

Quick Answers
Practice 23
pages 62–63
1. 42   9   9
2. 20   39   800
3. $60 $30 $1.30
4. $.53 $56 $125
5. 243 pages
6. $240

Using Circle Graphs
Practice 24
pages 64–65
1. 9%   2. 11%
3. .11 × 30,000 = **3,300 acres**   4. .53 × 30,000 = **15,900 acres**
5. .09 × 42,000 = **3,780 acres**   6. 53% + 11% = **64%**
7. .11 × 42,000 = **4,620 acres**   8. .174 × $2,300 = **$400.20**
9. .06 × $3,150 = **$189**   10. .17 × $460 = **$78.20**
11. .069 × $31,200 = **$2,152.80**   12. .069 × $2,200 = **$151.80**

Interest
Practice 25
pages 67–68

A.
  1. $30
  3. $66
  5. $375
  7. $46

        2. $120
        4. $33.60
        6. $29.25

B.
  8. $12
10. $35
12. $225
14. $270

        9. $40
      11. $20
      13. $67.50
      15. $15.75

Multi-Step Problem
Practice 26
pages 70–71

1. $.09 \times \$22{,}350 = \$2{,}011.50$

$$\begin{array}{r} \$22{,}350.00 \\ +\quad 2{,}011.50 \\ \hline \mathbf{\$24{,}361.50} \end{array}$$

2. $.06 \times \$19.85 = \$1.191$

$$\begin{array}{r} \$19.85 \\ +\quad 1.19 \\ \hline \mathbf{\$21.04} \end{array}$$

3. $.18 \times \$424 = \$76.32$

$$\begin{array}{r} \$424.00 \\ -\quad 76.32 \\ \hline \mathbf{\$347.68} \end{array}$$

4. $.2 \times \$.92 = \$.184$

$$\begin{array}{r} \$.92 \\ -\quad .18 \\ \hline \mathbf{\$.74} \end{array}$$

5. $.9 \times 80 = 72$

$$\begin{array}{r} 80 \\ -\ 72 \\ \hline \mathbf{8\ questions} \end{array}$$

6. $2.5 \times 24 = 60$

$$\begin{array}{r} 24 \\ +\ 60 \\ \hline \mathbf{84\ women} \end{array}$$

7. $.15 \times 220 = 33$

$$\begin{array}{r} 220 \\ - \quad 33 \\ \hline 187 \text{ pounds} \end{array}$$

8. $.08 \times \$24.49 = \$1.9592$

$$\begin{array}{r} \$24.49 \\ + \quad 1.96 \\ \hline \$26.45 \end{array}$$

9. $\frac{1}{4} \times 840 = 210$

$$\begin{array}{r} 840 \\ - \quad 210 \\ \hline 630 \text{ children} \end{array}$$

10. $\frac{1}{6} \times 24¢ = 4¢$

$$\begin{array}{r} 24¢ \\ - \quad 4¢ \\ \hline 20¢ \end{array}$$

11. $.16 \times 250 = 40$

$$\begin{array}{r} 250 \\ + \quad 40 \\ \hline \$290 \text{ billion} \end{array}$$

12. $.2 \times \$24.90 = \$4.98$

$$\begin{array}{r} \$24.90 \\ - \quad 4.98 \\ \hline \$19.92 \end{array}$$

13. $.12 \times \$132,500 = \$15,900$

$$\begin{array}{r} \$132,500 \\ - \quad 15,900 \\ \hline \$116,600 \end{array}$$

14. $.2 \times \$.89 = \$.178$

$$\begin{array}{r} \$ .89 \\ + \quad .18 \\ \hline \$1.07 \end{array}$$

15. $.10 \times 210 = 21$

$$\begin{array}{r} 210 \\ + \quad 21 \\ \hline 231 \text{ days} \end{array}$$

16. $.35 \times 12,800 = 4,480$

$$\begin{array}{r} \$ 12,800 \\ - \quad 4,480 \\ \hline \$8,320 \end{array}$$

Finding the Part Review
pages 72–74

1. 31.5
2. 92
3. 45
4. 30
5. 18
6. 21
7. $120
8. 756 families
9. $.84
10. $.19
11. 2.6
12. 6.75
13. 552
14. 9,000
15. 8.9%
16. 16,524
17. 2,712
18. $74.40
19. $27.75
20. .25 × $149 = $37.25

$$\begin{array}{r} \$149.00 \\ -37.25 \\ \hline \mathbf{\$111.75} \end{array}$$

21. .075 × $169 = $12.675

$$\begin{array}{r} \$169.00 \\ +12.68 \\ \hline \mathbf{\$181.68} \end{array}$$

Finding What Percent One Number Is of Another
Practice 27
pages 76–78

A.

1. 20% $66\frac{2}{3}\%$

2. 60%   75%

3. 50%   40%

4. 70% $37\frac{1}{2}\%$

5. 80% $83\frac{1}{3}\%$

6. 25%   7. $12\frac{1}{2}\%$

8. 80%   9. 20%

10. 6%

B.

11. 125%   250%

12. $166\frac{2}{3}\%$ $137\frac{1}{2}\%$

13. 220%   300%

14. 100%   200%

15. 300%   225%

16. 140%   17. $187\frac{1}{2}\%$

18. 300%   19. 1100%

20. 88%   21. 5%

22. 98%   23. 75%

Using Proportion to Find the Percent
Practice 28
pages 79–80

1. 20% $31\frac{1}{4}$%

2. 75%   35%
3. 10%   50%

4. 90% $87\frac{1}{2}$%

5. 9% $12\frac{1}{2}$%

6. 12%   250%

7. 85%   8. 12%

9. $33\frac{1}{3}$%   10. $37\frac{1}{2}$%

11. $62\frac{1}{2}$%   12. 85%

13. 280%

Percent of Increase
Practice 29
pages 81–82

1. $36 - 24 = 12$ $\frac{12}{24} = \frac{1}{2} = \textbf{50\%}$

2. $40 - 35 = 5$ $\frac{5}{35} = \frac{1}{7} = \textbf{14}\frac{2}{7}\textbf{\%}$

3. $96 - 60 = 36$ $\frac{36}{60} = \frac{3}{5} = \textbf{60\%}$

4. $84 - 63 = 21$ $\frac{21}{63} = \frac{1}{3} = \textbf{33}\frac{1}{3}\textbf{\%}$

5. $228 - 120 = 108$ $\frac{108}{120} = \frac{9}{10} = \textbf{90\%}$

6. $\$418 - \$380 = \$38$ $\frac{38}{380} = \frac{1}{10} = \textbf{10\%}$

7. $20 - 16 = 4$ $\frac{4}{16} = \frac{1}{4} = \textbf{25\%}$

8. $\$486 - \$450 = \$36$ $\frac{36}{450} = \frac{2}{25} = \textbf{8\%}$

9. $330,000 - 240,000 = 90,000$ $\frac{90,000}{240,000} = \frac{3}{8} = \textbf{37}\frac{1}{2}\textbf{\%}$

10. $63 - 18 = 45$ $\frac{45}{18} = \frac{5}{2} = \textbf{250\%}$

11. $\$8.68 - \$6.20 = \$2.48$ $\frac{2.48}{6.20} = \frac{2}{5} = \textbf{40\%}$

12. $\$1.50 - \$1.25 = \$.25$ $\frac{.25}{1.25} = \frac{1}{5} = \textbf{20\%}$

Percent of Decrease
Practice 30
pages 83–84

1. $80 - 60 = 20$ $\frac{20}{80} = \frac{1}{4} = 25\%$

2. $90 - 81 = 9$ $\frac{9}{90} = \frac{1}{10} = 10\%$

3. $200 - 120 = 80$ $\frac{80}{200} = \frac{2}{5} = 40\%$

4. $320 - 80 = 240$ $\frac{240}{320} = \frac{3}{4} = 75\%$

5. $\$840 - \$560 = \$280$ $\frac{280}{840} = \frac{1}{3} = 33\frac{1}{3}\%$

6. $\$1{,}200 - \$1{,}140 = \$60$ $\frac{60}{1200} = \frac{1}{20} = 5\%$

7. $20 - 11 = 9$ $\frac{9}{20} = 45\%$

8. $\$24 - \$16 = \$8$ $\frac{8}{24} = \frac{1}{3} = 33\frac{1}{3}\%$

9. $132 - 120 = 12$ $\frac{12}{132} = \frac{1}{11} = 9\frac{1}{11}\%$

10. $\$150 - \$132 = \$18$ $\frac{18}{150} = \frac{3}{25} = 12\%$

11. $128 - 96 = 32$ $\frac{32}{128} = \frac{1}{4} = 25\%$

12. $\$620 - \$434 = \$186$ $\frac{186}{620} = \frac{3}{10} = 30\%$

Finding a Number When a Percent of It Is Given
Practice 31
pages 86–87

1. 150   120
2. 330   250
3. 76   150
4. 85   56
5. 54   800
6. 48   160
7. 270 members   8. $530
9. 5,910 tickets   10. $1,800
11. 45   1,248
12. 20   200
13. 320   325
14. 4,000   56
15. 6,400   5,000
16. 150 bicycles   17. $89
18. 40 problems   19. $2,500
20. $435

Using Proportion to Find the Whole
Practice 32
pages 88–89

1. 52 150
2. 890 180
3. 400 300
4. 275 400
5. 1,200 400
6. 32.5 400
7. 80 games   8. 2,200 children
9. 51,250 people   10. 24 pounds
11. $1,943   12. 50 tons

Mixed Problems
Practice 33
pages 90–92

1. B $\frac{14}{28} = \frac{1}{2} = 50\%$
2. A $.6 \times 125 = 75$
3. B $\frac{60}{90} = \frac{2}{3} = 66\frac{2}{3}\%$
4. B $\frac{6}{120} = \frac{1}{20} = 5\%$
5. A $.8 \times 15 = 12$
6. C $13 \div .25 = 52$
7. B $\frac{270}{360} = \frac{3}{4} = 75\%$
8. A $.95 \times 400 = 380$
9. C $11 \div .2 = 55$
10. B $\frac{15}{75} = \frac{1}{5} = 20\%$
11. B $\frac{16}{48} = \frac{1}{3} = 33\frac{1}{3}\%$
12. A $.025 \times 300 = 7.5$
13. B $\frac{\$490}{\$1960} = \frac{1}{4} = 25\%$
14. A $.06 \times \$44 = \$2.64$
15. C $90 \div .75 = 120$ tickets
16. A $.75 \times 80 = 60$ questions
17. B $\frac{11}{20} = 55\%$
18. C $\$16 \div .8 = \$20$
19. A $.03 \times \$3,500,000 = \$105,000$
20. C $\$72,000 \div .6 = \$120,000$
21. B $\frac{\$27}{\$540} = \frac{1}{20} = 5\%$
22. A $.84 \times 650 = 546$ employees
23. A $.06 \times \$5,300 = \$318$
24. B $\frac{\$2,688}{\$16,800} = \frac{4}{25} = 16\%$

Finding the Percent and the Whole Review
pages 93–94

1. $\frac{27}{36} = \frac{3}{4} = 75\%$
2. $\frac{45}{50} = \frac{9}{10} = 90\%$
3. $\frac{78}{130} = \frac{6}{10} = 60\%$
4. $\frac{72}{40} = \frac{9}{5} = 180\%$
5. $\frac{12}{40} = \frac{3}{10} = 30\%$
6. $\frac{\$110}{\$2,200} = \frac{1}{20} = 5\%$
7. $36 - 32 = 4$ $\frac{4}{32} = \frac{1}{8} = 12\frac{1}{2}\%$
8. $588 - 420 = 168$ $\frac{168}{420} = \frac{2}{5} = 40\%$
9. $\$480 - \$320 = \$160$ $\frac{160}{320} = \frac{1}{2} = 50\%$
10. $75 - 60 = 15$ $\frac{15}{75} = \frac{1}{5} = 20\%$

11. $720 - 480 = 240$ $\dfrac{240}{720} = \dfrac{1}{3} = 33\dfrac{1}{3}\%$

12. $\$380 - \$323 = \$57$ $\dfrac{57}{380} = \dfrac{3}{20} = 15\%$

13. $213 \div .75 = 284$
14. $21 \div .035 = 600$
15. $\$2,700 \div .6 = \$4,500$

Final Review
pages 95–99

1. 5:4
2. 4:9
3. 4:7
4. 5 to 3
5. 1:20
6. 3:8
7. 3:2
8. 90
9. $42\dfrac{1}{2}$
10. $2\dfrac{2}{3}$
11. 9 gallons
12. 260 miles
13. 26.2 mpg
14. 9 quarts
15. 2%
16. 47.5%
17. $9\dfrac{1}{3}\%$
18. .92
19. .04
20. .009
21. 48%
22. $41\dfrac{2}{3}\%$
23. $62\dfrac{1}{2}\%$ or 62.5%
24. $\dfrac{9}{25}$
25. $\dfrac{17}{200}$
26. $\dfrac{2}{7}$
27. 26
28. 70
29. 20
30. 140
31. 60
32. 2
33. 36 questions
34. $15,950
35. $.50
36. 20.5%
37. 12,408,000 vehicles
38. $208.25
39. $4,200,000
40. $54
41. $220
42. $37\dfrac{1}{2}\%$
43. 50%
44. 20%
45. $83\dfrac{1}{3}\%$
46. 15%
47. 6%
48. 36%
49. 12%
50. 48
51. 150
52. 40
53. 90
54. $2,506
55. 65 problems